ROS

PORTRAITS FROM A MIDLANDS CITY

ROSEHILL

PORTRAITS FROM A MIDLANDS CITY

CAROL LAKE

BLOOMSBURY

First published in Great Britain 1989
Copyright © 1989 by Carol Lake
This paperback edition published 1990
Illustration by Sylvia Whiteford-Engholm

Bloomsbury Publishing Ltd, 2 Soho Square, London W1V 5DE

British Library Cataloguing in Publication Data

Lake, Carol
Rosehill: Portraits from a Midlands City
1. Derbyshire. Derby. Social life. Biographies
I. Title
942.5'170858'0924

ISBN 0-7475-0578-0

10 9 8 7 6 5 4 3 2 1

Grateful acknowledgement is made to
Warner Chappell Music Ltd for
permission to reproduce two lines
from 'Blowin' In The Wind' by Bob Dylan.

Typeset by Hewer Text Composition Services, Edinburgh
Printed in Great Britain by Richard Clay Ltd, Bungay, Suffolk

Rosehill: a twilight corner of a Midlands city — decaying, poor;
known to outsiders by reputation, not acquaintance. St Andrew's
church is now St Andrew's house, dispensing Giros by way of
salvation, and the vicarage belongs to the social services
department. All around, homes have been destroyed, with only
their wild gardens left, as if in memory.

But the villas in Rosehill Street are still standing, and the
council-owned houses nearby. The school building remains,
though it's now a community centre, and the 'I-love-you' tree from
childhood grows on. Alongside the small shops and pubs a new
mosque glistens white in the sun. Birds sing in the arboretum; even
here, the seasons change.

The voices of children at play can be heard, Roxana and Emmaline,
Dean and Polly. Mohammed lives in Rosehill, kindly landlord, still
a friend. Half-Somalian Hawa lived here too, in happier times, and
old, eccentric Mr Sandman. Young Ahmed's round the corner,
always dropping in with jokes and tales of Pakistan. Mrs Holmes is
next door and Sassy's at The Old Rose Revived, nerves on edge with
family worries, generous-hearted, known for years. Other people
offer joy and consolation; hopes and dreams retain their fragile
hold.

In this collection of linked stories, Carol Lake paints a haunting
picture of the contemporary inner city. Her rich sense of character
transcends all stereotype as she pays gentle tribute to the triumph
of the human spirit.

These stories were written and take place between the autumn of 1985 and December 1986 (with the exception of 'Hawa' and 'At Mohammed's').
They began when Karl Miller asked me to write a diary piece for the *London Review of Books*. It was September 1985, and the Handsworth riots had just happened. Professor Miller felt it might be interesting to hear from someone who had lived in an inner city area for some time. After this, Xandra Hardie, my literary agent, suggested I write some more pieces, and gave me lots of encouragement. And that is how they began.
'Signing On' first appeared in the *London Review of Books*. 'The Sisters' has been published in *New Statesman & Society*.
The names of the people portrayed have been changed.

CL

CONTENTS

SIGNING ON

O N WEDNESDAY MORNINGS I fall out of bed in a hurry because I have to go to the labour exchange to sign on. Check obsessively that I have my key, slam the door and hurry off. Tear through the park – I love the park, it's more or less the same as it was when I used to walk through it going to school, years ago. It's landscaped, but when I'm flying through it to get to the labour exchange on time I don't linger to admire the scenery. Every time I go past the fountain near where Henry Royce's statue used to stand, I mutter and tick away to myself, 'Fkin bastids fkin bastids fkin bastids.' I saw that on a wall once and always think it like that now; it seems to express something inchoate and furious. The council came and took away the statue, which had always been there, and put it outside the Council House.

There are lots of people signing on, lots of queues. The unemployment rate in the town is 14 per cent. In this area it's 37.7 per cent. I don't usually speak to anybody. About eighteen months ago there was a big row and discussion about unemployment in the queues, with everybody chipping in. If I see any of the people that took part we smile and nod and exchange a few words. Otherwise I don't speak to anybody. There's nothing to say. On the wall near the door a teenager has scratched 'Have I survived school dinners for this?'. Last time I came there was a test-check on me. That means they ask all the questions over again, just to check you haven't worked or moved. The supervisor who did it turned out to be a girl I went to the juniors with – it was a bit embarrassing. We both smiled very slightly and looked away. She didn't make it difficult.

I push the card through – I like to date it myself, it's one way of keeping in touch with the date, but sometimes they stamp it automatically. Just as I'm leaving a voice hails me, 'Hey up there, Paddy.' It's my friend, Kay. She calls me Paddy because I'm not Irish. It's her joke.

'I'm late again.'

I say I'll wait for her. At the gates I stand around, pulling up my coat collar and stamping a little. A youth is standing there too, chirping out the name of a Marxist paper at everybody. Nobody buys any. I used to be in one of those groups. Actually our lot couldn't stick his lot but it's a long time ago and I feel a bit sorry for him, his heart's in the right place, so I say pleasantly (I think), 'You're not selling any because when people sign on they're at the end of their money.' I mean it quite kindly, so he shan't be depressed about it all.

He takes instant and total umbrage at this; he looks at me fiercely through thick spectacles and says, 'As a matter of fact we are selling them. As a matter of fact our sales figures are the best they've ever been, so I'm not depressed about it at all. As a matter of fact, I've sold quite a few this morning.'

This is such a manifest lie, that I don't bother with it. 'Oh good.'

When I stay in the house for a long time and don't see anybody, and then go out again, everybody looks peculiar. It's nothing to do with age, nationality, looks, it's just that all the passing faces look slightly grotesque, and alike in their peculiarity. Me and Kay move off to Woolworth's cafeteria, passing an abandoned joke-shop, where an old sign still reads 'A Laugh a Day Keeps the Crisis at Bay'. Uh-huh. It's been there about eight years.

In Woolworth's we make ourselves comfortable, because we usually stay for about two hours, sipping and nattering. All around us the teacups pile up, customers come and go, girls with pot-trolleys smile indulgently – I suppose they wouldn't do if the place was small, but it seems acres wide, and rarely fills up. I like Kay, we've known each other for two years now, through signing on. She's Irish, and very jolly, even when she's really down. She used to look terrible, the first winter we met, she was coming off heroin and her guy had just left her. Ashen and lined, clutching her fur jacket about her and smoking copiously, she talked and laughed, and talked more. Now she is totally changed, just the laugh is left. She lards her sentences with 'And I said to him – I've given up everything for Love', which always makes me grin, and then she grins, and we sit there grinning at each other like fools. Next time she is going to tell me what happened when she went to a spiritualist.

In the evening Sassy and her small children and I walk about among the ruined houses round the corner, finding plants, just looking. We've known each other since we were small; we used to play around these streets and go down them now remembering people who lived in the houses and talking about what became of them, and things we did long ago. I don't think there's anything sadder than seeing the little gardens that people have cared for and tended for years laid desolate and wild, waiting to be bulldozed. As we stand on Rosehill Street with dirty hands and arms full of grubbed-up marigolds and garden poppies, a small solemn procession of men leave the new mosque. I see my ex-landlord, Mohammed, with head ritually shaven and bowed. I don't wave at him or hoot across the road Hi there, Mohammed because we look thoroughly disreputable, our hair blowing about, legs and shoes dusty, and the children quarrelling.

On Fridays my Giro comes, and a form from the council saying the rent is going up. This doesn't affect those on the dole, because Social Security pay the rent directly to the council – it doesn't pass through claimants' hands. On the back of the form is a set of rules about only using the property as a private dwelling, care of dwelling and garden, nuisance to neighbours, including harassment, whether racial or otherwise. The last bit is underlined, which infuriates me. I'm not talking about the clause itself, because I agree with it – but about the fact that somebody has stood in the housing department and underlined it, as though we're all in need of correction and moral guidance, from somebody who almost certainly doesn't live round here. Well, that just takes the biscuit. What's it supposed to do, anyway? If you get on with your neighbours, then it's superfluous, and if you don't, holding up a stern verbal finger whilst keeping well clear – that's not likely to make things better.

Hare off round town quickly, and take in a gas instalment. Outside the Gas Board a boy plays an accordion. On the pavement chalk bluebirds fly about, but bikes have been run through them, leaving blue hoops behind. Now comes the real hard part – food shopping. Wandering around among the counters I lose my appetite completely. Over on the meat counter there's a saddle of lamb for £12.85. I look at this curiosity like it's in a museum, have absolutely no desire to eat it. Even if I had the money, I wouldn't spend it on that. If I stayed too long here, I could throw up. Especially when you come out and there on a hoarding is the picture of a bag of bones that should be a baby. Sometimes I wonder if the Third World will ever be allowed to be anything but hungry, while the industrialised countries still have their inner hunger. The image of starvation is maybe too near what people in this country feel like inside.

Coming back from town, I see Mrs Holmes, the lady next door, standing on her doorstep. She shows me her knitting. She's had migraine badly, so could only manage to cable two-thirds up and knit the rest plain, but it looks fine. She's lived here for over thirty years, and she's waiting on the step for her son. He grew up round here and passed lots of exams, and got a good job, and now he comes to see her every day in a big silver car.

The man next door on the other side, Mr Shaw, has been altering their passageway, and putting up wooden panels. He's getting on a bit, so only does it now and then, when he feels like it. He showed me last week – it should be quite good. He has made lots of alterations to the house over the years, and it looks bigger inside as a result. The Shaws came from the West Indies a long time ago. Mrs Shaw is blind now. She stays in the house all the time, and not many people in the street have seen her. I've only seen her twice – on Sundays, getting in the car to go to church.

There's a fearful banging on the door. It's Ahmed. He comes straight from mosque, dumps his cap and book on the mantelpiece and makes for the carrier bags in the kitchen, scratching about in them.

'Oooo, chocolate cake.'

'You can just come out of there. You're not having any. Muslims can't eat chocolate cake, it's not allowed.'

'They can. They can, Carol. That's what Muslims can eat.'

'Oh I see, Mohammed told you, did he, he put it in the Koran: all Muslims must eat chocolate cake on Fridays?'

'Yes, he did,' he says, stoutly optimistic. He doesn't believe for a minute that he won't get any cake.

Gail comes round. She is mad about the council forms, reserves the same contempt for them that soldiers in the front line had for their superior officers back home.

'It makes me sick. They all live out of town and God knows where. They don't live round here, that's for sure.'

Gail is friendly, she was the first person to invite me in for a cup of tea when I moved here.

Unemployed, harassed, she lives with her teenage son, and, when she's not hauling in a line full of washing at the back, she's rinsing her sparkling windows at the front. She is very houseproud.

I like Gail, but she's crazy. You won't believe this, but when her and Surinder, who lives next door to her, had a row, Gail reported her to the Cats' Protection League for not having her tom-cat neutered. She told me that herself. But they are friends again now: Gail bangs Surinder up in the night to unlock the entry, when she's forgotten her front door key.

Sunday in the garden. It's very quiet and full of sunshine, and roses flaming orange and red, like a flowery furnace, and clusters of blackberries all along the wall. The whole garden is wild – I just haven't trimmed it at all, although I did plant a pear tree two years ago, which is still battling to survive. I stand talking to one of the Shaw girls, and she's telling me about her sister who has plum trees and makes jam. Two of the younger sisters come out, nod, and one of them says something about wogs, just loud enough for me to hear. They laugh under their breaths together. I've never said anything like that to any of them, so I just ignore her, the cheeky little sod.

On Monday morning I get up, put on the kettle, light the grill for toast, trip over the cat's plate, curse, and switch on the wireless, straight into the news. It's all about Handsworth. Bloody hell. Straightaway switch it right down – I don't know why, I just don't want any of the neighbours to know I'm listening to it. Late in the morning a house across the way blasts a record out for about three minutes and then there's silence again. Later Mrs Holmes and Gail and Surinder come out, all talking.

This sounds awful, I know, but I get fed up with hearing rotten news, so don't always listen. And I'm glad I haven't got television. Not many people I know watch television much actually, unless they have small children, and then it's switched on to amuse them. It's to do with not being able to sit still and watch other people when you want to get on with your own affairs. The only time during the news about Handsworth that I regretted not having a television was when that government minister went there and then had to run off. But you can't have everything, and it was a small treat hearing about it. It was awful about the people who died.

'Yes, everybody's dead mad about it,' says Ahmed.

'Did you see the rioting on television?'

'Yes – well, some of it. Then my mum got cross and said, "I'm sick of this all the time," and switched it on to the other side.'

Sassy doesn't watch television much either.

'Yes, it's terrible,' she says vaguely. 'I don't watch much, I just can't do with it, it gets on my nerves, and if I watch it for too long I start picking up a code and then I don't know where I am. I don't even like to be in the same room when it's on . . . I mean, I have to be so very careful. I know there's a bug in here.'

She was nursing in the local mental hospital for years, and then she was taken in herself after she had her last baby. When she starts to talk like this, I always look doubtful – I don't know why, because I sometimes think that myself, although I don't tell her so. That's what happens when God drops down out of the sky – you're left with an ugly little bug. For months, one time, I thought I was being followed round by a red car. Every time I went out there was this same red car. It was even there several times over, and sometimes it had a black roof, but it was the same car, following me. I'd see it parked, turn a corner, and there it was again. It's easy to say they were all different cars

– I knew that then. They were different but they weren't. A boy who used to live in the next bedsitter to mine a few years ago had spent seven months seeing cross-eyes. Every person he looked at appeared to be cross-eyed.

'I kept rubbing my eyes because I knew it couldn't be like that. But I couldn't get rid of it.'

None of this has anything to do with drugs. When I came out of the mental hospital and walked about I'd turn a corner of a street I knew and instead of the well-known street there would be ruins. This happened so many times that places that were still standing I'd see as ruins. Destruction by mobs round here won't be any novelty. It's been happening for years.

Ahmed comes round. It's Saturday and he's spent all morning looking for a man who changes the colour of your shoes. He says there's been a big Sikh procession in Rosehill Street, men with swords on floats.

'Like May Day, you mean?'

'I don't know. They didn't look very pleased. They're still mad about Mrs Gandhi.'

He's wearing a spell rolled round and sewn into a piece of white linen. It's a magic word that only the man who wrote it can understand. Ahmed's mother brought it back from Pakistan, to stop him from having bad dreams.

'And does it work?'

'Yes, I think so. When I wear it. I don't always wear it. Sometimes I like a change.'

He agitates to go shopping, in town. I hate shopping. Pass a billboard with its headlines for the local paper: 'DRUG YOUTH FOUND HANGED' . . . In town, where priorities are different, a board advertising the same paper announces 'LOCAL DJ ACCUSED OF FIDDLING'. Drug-taking and glue-sniffing are apparently a big problem round here. Since being at his new school Ahmed's constant conversation is about drugs.

I hate shopping. There's nothing in the shops I want. In a shop window there's a jacket knitted in a tartan design. The idea of knitted tartan amuses and intrigues me. I examine it closely to see how the illusion is achieved. But I have no desire to own it. Stop wanting – an answer to the problem of living on social security? Not really, because if lots of people just looked at things instead of desiring them, then looking would become stealing, and people would be in the wrong for doing it. Sometimes I don't even want to look at things, as though that's already the case.

Through Wednesday night I lie in bed hearing police sirens blaring. That's no surprise – the local team are playing Leicester. The next day headlines in the local paper announce a full-scale riot, at The Cambridge, a nearby pub. Windows were smashed and cars burnt out. Apparently, people were leaving the match while it was going on, to join in the commotion outside.

I stand at the sink washing the pots. About six yards away the friendly Shaw sister picks berries on the wall. We wave to one another enthusiastically, like we're miles away. In her garden Mrs Holmes stands wondering over her beans. In spite of the lousy summer Gail's sweetpeas have fought their way to the top of the wall.

When the news about Brixton comes through, Mr Shaw next door starts banging on the wall, doing his alterations. He hasn't touched them for weeks. As the evening wears on, he thumps away. At one point it sounds as though he must come through the wall. The newsreels are maybe making him feel energetic. If they keep the rioting going for a bit longer, maybe he'll finish his hallway. He's still thundering away at twenty to twelve. I hitch up my nightdress, put a skirt on over it, and saunter out to the chip shop.

'What will Hawa and Teddy be doing – will they be in the riots?' asks Ahmed. He's never met them, only heard me speak of them. We all used to be Mohammed's tenants for four years, but haven't met for ages.

'They've got a young family now, so I shouldn't think for one minute they'll be anywhere but at home.'

I know what Teddy will be doing, though. He'll be sitting in front of the television, chuckling. Appalled, but chuckling. I may be wrong. But I don't think so. I remember one Saturday a couple of years back, before I moved here. When the football crowds passed they went down the street smashing all the windows. All the houses were empty, awaiting demolition, except mine and next door. I wasn't at all scared but when night came I did get a bit scared, because I was living alone in two streets of empty houses, with an old lady next door, and now the front windows were out. When I heard thumping at the door my heart sank a little. I looked out from upstairs.

It's Hawa – she's in carpet slippers and has left her month-old baby to run down four empty streets to come here. Her voice floats up. I peer out at her dark face in the darkness.

'We heard about your windows, Carol. Teddy says he'll come and put them in for you.'

Sassy hates buses, she walks everywhere, she likes to feel the ground under her feet.

'I don't like buses, I don't really feel I've gone anywhere.'

Every year when her daughter Paula was small they both walked across town, to the only Church May Day that was left.

'Even that's gone now. And it made a nice day for the children. I used to dress Paula up in a little pale green dress with a wreath of flowers, and we joined the procession.'

There's a photograph on the wall of six-year-old Paula, with hair-ribbons and bunches, and flower-circlet. It's only ten years ago. Under all the white chalk Paula dowses on herself you can just make out the same little face.

'She gets her Giro, goes out and crashes it straightaway, and then she lies in bed all day reading horror stories, when she's not running wild with a lot of black girls. And they do get up to some things. They take things from shops and goodness knows what. I'm not talking about, how shall I say – *stealing* – like, done *secret*. They just all march into the shop together and take what they like. Quite open. Nobody stops them. It's terrible. I got this blouse from them, because they sell stuff at back doors . . .'

It's Sunday evening and warm for the time of year. I go upstairs early in the evening, drawing the curtains. Across the street see Trisha is putting her little boys to bed. Through the open window the street noises come in, through the thin curtains, and the singing from the pub on the corner. 'We're off to Dublin in the green, in the green . . .' News comes over the wireless that there's more rioting, in London. Tottenham, I think they said. I switch off. Later, when the cats are put to bed and the light is off, I lie in bed, hearing the comforting usual sounds of the street. About two weekends ago a man walked up and down the street barking out the Ten Commandments. Every time he got to 'Thou shalt not commit adultery' he went potty shouting and screaming it. It makes a change from Joc-wi'-no-fingers, who strides through the warm dark streets shouting drunkenly, 'Blacks – can yuh hear me? I killed for yuh . . .' Sometimes he has a woman with him, and then they shout and scream at each other instead. But tonight it's quiet, just a singing straggler from the corner pub, and the clinking of milk bottles as one of the Shaws puts out the empties on the step.

Gail, who has just started work in The Mafeking round the corner, tells me that while the rioting was going on in Tottenham on Sunday, round the corner at the bottom of the street thousands of Sikhs converged on the *gurdwara*, which has been occupied by supporters of Khalistan for months. The original more moderate section has got a court order to evict them. Gail wasn't allowed to go home; she had to stay in the pub until seven o'clock the next morning because the whole area was sealed off by police.

'There was police there from five different forces, even the Metropolitan. The Sikhs wore orange turbans and they came into the pub with their swords and ripped out the phone. There was absolutely thousands of them. I wasn't scared. Well, I was a bit when they set fire to something in the middle of the road. We were serving the Sikhs, then we were serving the police . . .'

As she's talking, I start to wonder if she's lying about there having been thousands of Sikhs just round the corner. It just seems so incredible not to have known. If there's one thing in the world I value, it's the capacity to be rational, which used to seem very dull. But if you're let loose into a series of nightmares you come to value it. I think of Graham, battling to stand on his feet, knowing in his mind that *every* person couldn't have cross-eyes, yet still seeing them. And this is quite apart from the problem of drugs, or the problem of racism.

HAWA

IT HAS BEEN some time since I have seen Hawa Hussein – she's called something else now, but I always think of her as Hawa Hussein. We haven't seen a great deal of one another since we both had rooms at Mohammed's. I moved in seven years ago. In the winters, especially, when the world is slow and sleepy and dark, I get thinking back to that time.

I can feel very vividly the first day we became friends. It was late autumn. The summer that year had lasted well into October; wasps and insects batted about in my room in the roof, the sloping window was propped open to the full by an old chair leg, and short sleeves were still being worn in the warm summer streets. But this day was the first rainy day, although still warm. It was a Thursday. I had done a little shopping in town, and was strolling back through the damp park, swinging a Sainsbury's carrier. Hidden in my bag like fruits was a book on Venice (where I had never been), a book which I had coveted for some weeks. I had been slipping into the second-hand bookshop and tasting snippets of it, and was anticipating further delights when I reached my room. Overhead, the trees from my childhood dripped moisture on to me, and a slight mist held the far trees. I was happy. I had no man, no child, no job, no anything that I could think of. Yet I was strangely happy all the time that sunny autumn. Over the grass under the far avenue of limes rolled a man in an invalid carriage. I could remember him from a long time ago.

At this time I had been back in the town for a couple of months, and had a room at the top of a house in a street well known to me. At first I had strolled about – the streets of my childhood seemed like the streets out of a dream. Very many were down, and those that were left standing were tinned up or surrounded by ruins. But the school was still there. When people in town asked me where I came from, and I said Rosehill, a slight shadow, almost a sudden abstraction seemed to pass across their faces.

On Rosehill Street there was a paper shop, which still carried pencilled and biroed notices for rooms and flats to let, and I had looked amongst them through the old panes. This had been an afternoon, for in the mornings, as I subsequently saw, there was often an old man standing nearby, directing lookers for rooms to his own house or his relations' houses. The address I selected was one near my old school, where I had been very happy. I had nothing else to guide me.

When I got there and rang the bell, a man came out and shook his head. No, no rooms. Not to let? The notice was wrong? Wrong. Then where should I go? He hesitated then. Well, there might be a room. Just a minute. He went back into the house. A toddler stood on the doorstep, chattering down at her bright red – and obviously new – shoes, entranced, dazed by their great beauty. She chattered away at them, speaking not just baby-language, but a tongue unknown to me. The man returned wearing a small embroidered hat, and he said, without any great enthusiasm but with some purpose, 'Come.'

We went to a house two streets away, his brother's house. The room to let was the attic, which I wanted at once, though it was bare except for a small dressing-table and a huge old bed, splattered about with bird droppings from the open window in the roof.

'Rent – how much, do you think? £7?'

'I don't know, I was thinking more like five,' I said involuntarily.

'Six, six,' he sang out at once, and I saw that I had unwittingly entered into a haggle, which I hate doing, and in fact can't do, but this had been so easy that it had happened regardless, as though my will was on castors underneath me and was running away. I realised he would rather the rent be £6 and the result of haggle, a participation, than £7 and me merely consenting to his demand. The man, slight of figure and faultlessly polite, was called Mohammed Latif – Mr Latif. His brother was a tall, substantial figure who spoke English much less well, and he was also called Mohammed.

During the week the second Mohammed worked shifts; on Fridays – shifts permitting – he went to the mosque; on Saturdays he cleaned the kitchen and then went into town; and on Sundays lots of his relations descended upon the house. The other rooms in the house were let – an old man, Mr Sandman, but usually called the Old Man, had a room, and the ground floor was occupied by a young black couple, Hal and Teddy. I'd seen little more of Teddy than a Rasta cap and an affable grin at the door, but Hal was around in the daytime, she floated about the house in long diaphanous blue, and at half-past three each afternoon she went into the kitchen to prepare their evening meal, to be ready for when Teddy got home from work at five o'clock. She seemed quite pleasant.

As I walked under the trees in the park in a sweet melancholy, there was a niggle in the back of my mind. Two days before, on my way to sign on, I was walking down a park pathway, behind two women and a small boy, about four years old. The middle-aged woman was saying loudly and furiously, 'I'm just about fed up with it, having to collect him from school all the time. His mother can't be bothered with him, his father can't be bothered with him. They don't want him, that's what it amounts to. Well *I* don't want him . . .' She announced this to anybody who was around to hear, including the child himself – 'I don't want him.'

'It's not as though he behaves himself,' agreed the teenage girl, who was as fat and waddling as the woman. As I passed them, turning to stare quite openly, I saw the small boy had his eyes lowered as they were exchanging fury over him, marching him between them and keeping up a constant verbal torrent.

Afterwards I felt that I should have said something, but thought I should at least tell someone at the school, a small nursery known locally as the threepenny bit-school because of its hexagonal shape. Two days had passed, and I still hadn't done anything. As I walked past the school, I knew I wouldn't ever tell anybody. Then I turned round and traced my steps back through the park, and went in.

When I arrive back at Mohammed's and let myself into the dark hall, it seems darker and gloomier than usual, and when I hear the sound of pots in the kitchen I feel a sudden need for company.

'Hi.'

'Hi.'

I dump my carrier and reach up to the rack to pull down a towel which I've washed that morning. The girl from downstairs peers into her large pan, sizzling with garlic and butter, adds the meat, and then sits, ready to be chatty, on the chest of drawers.

'Honestly! I've just been up to a school to report this woman I saw, telling a child that his parents didn't want him and nobody wanted him – a small child, you know. And when I told the headmistress, she was perfectly polite but she acted like it was me that was nuts.'

The girl's eyes get big and then bigger. Then she says straightaway, 'When I was little, in Africa, people were cruel to me. My grown-up brother was awful to me. He was so cruel to me, he used to make me sit cross-legged on the floor for hours and hours, without moving.' She glares, suddenly resentful. 'He was cruel to me and I hated him, and I said to him once, "I'll never forget how you've treated me, you've treated me like a slave, not a sister." And he used to jeer at me . . .' She is speaking with a sudden leap into passion, as though it had happened last week. She talks on, and suddenly there is the front door opening.

'My God, it's Teddy. Will you come down for a cup of coffee with me tomorrow?'

I agree enthusiastically. It's Mohammed, coming through the front door. He strides into the kitchen, and I nod. 'See you tomorrow then, Hal.'

'My *real* name's Hawa,' she says.

'Ah – Hawa – the first she. Adam's she,' says Mohammed.

'*My* name means spices,' insists Hawa scornfully.

'Adam's she,' repeats Mohammed definitely.

In the evenings, on his late shift, Mohammed trundles off out into what may be an alien night, with his knitted cap pulled down to keep out the cold, and clutching his tea flask. In the house, after about eleven o'clock, behind the front door the inner vestibule door is firmly closed. Soon after I moved in, Mohammed told me to make sure the inner door is closed at night, when he is at work.

'When I not here you will shut this door,' he says politely, thundering out each word separately. This isn't a request or an order, it's a statement. It's safer.

Up the tiny stairway carpeted in brown drugget – perhaps this was the maid's room many years ago – I climb, up, up, high above the house, floating, floating.

At the end of a long dark corridor is the bathroom, which is a large converted back bedroom. I love the bathroom, it is colourful, with very many kinds of wallpaper; and worn places have been patched over with all kinds of different squares of paper, with no attempt to match up designs. The paintwork is blue and yellow, and the cupboard housing the cistern looks as though someone painted half-way up, got bored with the colour, and immediately changed it on impulse. There is no attempt to observe the lines of door or frame, as though a sovereign will wielded the paintbrush. The whole room reminds me a little of a Matisse painting, a riot of blue and yellow, pink, pink and more pink; red. I always cheer up when I come in here.

Often, when home from work in the evenings, Mohammed doesn't put his light on; he sits listening to a tape which sounds like an Islamic Hitler shrieking into the dark. In the daytime the hall and landing are mostly quiet, and all up the stairs – silence. At the weekends, when the landlord is at home, there is a constant stream of children and women, cooking and screaming and dashing about. Mostly I stay in my room and eat cold stuff, but sometimes slip down the two flights of stairs to the kitchen, to heat soup or boil an egg.

'I'm not working just now, but I'm really a model,' says Hawa with a flap of lash when we meet the next day.

'I'm really a writer,' I say back, just as seriously. We look at one another, and burst out laughing. She is very beautiful, with long eyelashes, blue-black hair, tiny delicate hands and face, which make her seem small when she is sitting. She is actually quite tall and thin, and has a perfectly erect bearing without being rigid, not like a model, like an African Muslim.

'You don't sound African. Have you been here long?'

'I come from Somalia. My dad's Somali and my mum's English, but they live in Liverpool now. I don't see them, I haven't seen them since the summer, when I ran away from home. I was brought up in Somalia. When I was sixteen they made me marry a man who was nearly sixty, he was a friend of my parents, I'd known him for a long time. That sounds awful to you, I bet . . .' She breaks off, smiling, and I smile back. 'Well, it doesn't sound awful to me. I expected a husband that age, our tribe does . . . It was just *him* I didn't like.'

Hawa went to secondary school in Liverpool. 'It was real tough, Carol. I made some good friends there, though. This girl, she says to me – because there were these girls want'n' to fight me – she says, "Come on, I'm going to teach you to fight."

'I says, "I can fight."

'"No," she says, "not like them, you can't. They fight dirty. I'm going to show you some tricks . . ."'

Her husband had paid several hundred pounds, in expectation of the marriage, and Hawa's mother had used some of this to send her on a modelling course. Her husband was not always at home – they lived at Hawa's parents – and had soon left, leaving a very dissatisfied bride behind. He was gone nearly a year, during which time Hawa modelled during the day, went to discos and pubs with her old school friends in the evenings, and crossed her fingers he would be a long time coming back.

'I was dreading to hear he was coming, and when he got back the second time I didn't know how I was going to stand it. He'd brought us all presents and stuff.' She tosses the word out bitterly, scornfully. 'My mother thought everything would be all right; she said, "Try and understand him, try to be nice to him, he wants the best for you, we all do." But he wasn't nice to me, and when I wouldn't do what he wanted – in bed, you know – I *did* try at first, but I got fed up with him, and when I didn't do exactly what he told me he started hitting me, I got bruises on my face. That's when I knew I wasn't going to stop. After he'd gone back to sea I had a row with my mother. I'd seen Teddy around at discos and that, and I'd just started to get to know him a bit better, and I heard *he* was coming back. So I knew I couldn't stop. The night before I left I was talking in bed with my sisters, we were talking all night nearly about *everything*, but I never said anything about what I was going to do, and I thought: Well, I don't care, I don't care about anything, this time tomorrow I won't be here . . . The next day I met Teddy, and he'd borrowed a car, and we drove away and I've never been back. My mother didn't know where I was, but I didn't care, I didn't let her know, because it was her fault for making me marry *him*.

'My parents sent me to Africa when I was a baby. It wasn't safe here then – I was shot at in the streets, my mum's got all the newspaper cuttings about it. She was out shopping with her sister, and me, and my brother – he was about three, and they all had to run suddenly because these gangs of men chased them through the streets with guns. Afterwards, reporters and that came to take my photo. My parents decided it wasn't safe for us here. I can't remember any of it. I was only just over a year old when I was taken there. It was hard for my mum, she said it was, but she was thinking of us. All of the children went there, as soon as they were old enough to leave her. Not the two littlest ones, they've always been at home. Things had changed by then – it was safer, you know.

'It's funny to think of now.' She tips her head, and smiles, as though recalling a perplexing dream. 'I lived there and I had no idea about here, not really. I didn't come back here until I was eleven. My mother came for me on a plane, and I'd never seen her before. I did know I'd got other brothers and sisters, but I didn't know where they were – we were all sent to different places. I watched this white woman come down the stairs from the plane, and I thought: That's my mother, and I couldn't believe it. You know, Serah, my whole life hasn't been – like – *real*.'

(For a long time, easily a year – or perhaps a year and a day – Hawa always called me Sarah, or Serah, as she said it, sometimes breaking off, ' – I'm sorry, I know it isn't Serah, it's just I always think English girls are called that, I've got it in my mind – a real English girl called Serah,' and she taps sharply on her head with her fingers, as though to dislodge it.)

'I was sewn up,' she says, with a slight air of defiance.

'Sewn up?'

'Yes. It's what our tribe do. All my – down there – all on the outside, it was cut off when I was very small, and I was sewn up, so that nobody would get at me, until my husband.'

'Oh.'

Some time later in the dentist's waiting-room I skim quickly through an article – infibulation – female circumcision – Muslim Africa – baby girls – mutilation – dreadful . . .

'It's funny, you know,' she says quietly. 'I've had a lot of English friends, at school and afterwards, and they've all every one of them been shocked when I told them about it, they've all thought it was terrible. You're the only English person I've told who hasn't been shocked.'

'Well, I am shocked,' I reply evenly, truthfully. I hate to be stampeded into showing shock, but afterwards think perhaps it was a bit mean of me, because maybe she wants me to take the weight of outrage about it, so she can defend it and so not feel so bad about it. Although in a way there is a part of me that isn't shocked or moved at all, about anything.

'You see, you have to be out there, it's very deserted, and there's herdsmen and that; you know, you might be wandering in the countryside and there'd be nobody around. So it's protection for you, really. I know it sounds terrible, but I don't blame my mother – she gave her consent, she wanted us to be proper members of our tribe, she didn't want us to be like English.

'Before I got married, this woman come round, the night before, to take the stitches out. They were giving me things – drinks and that, but other stuff too, to make it easier, but my God, Serah, I've never known such pain. She had this big knife, I could have passed out just looking at it . . . But she knows how to do it so's there's no danger. It's a woman they send for specially at weddings in Liverpool, she does it the night before.

'I've got this cousin, Yvonne – I think black people having English names is very funny – '

'Yvonne is a French name.'

'Well, a white name, then.' She lifts her lip in pure scorn. 'Yvonne says, "Come on, Hawa, it'll be all right, get it over with," and *she's* not been done, she's always stayed safe over here . . .' As she talks, Hawa's different lives – African, Liverpudlian, slide about her like iridescence on a bubble.

On week-day afternoons Hawa climbs the little stairs, I put on the kettle, we hover, pause, then it's like we both jump into each other's lives and swim about. We sit drinking tea or salted coffee – Hawa's favourite – and nibbling at buttered toast or chocolate digestive biscuits. As we talk her face seems like dark moving water, casting back a pale sky and dark clouds of cypress.

I stand at the dressing-table, making another drink. A foot and a half away, Hawa sits in the one small chair in the room, talking.

'And one day when my brother was calling me – he really hated me, he was my half-brother, we had different mothers and he was grown-up – and he was saying you don't do this, you don't do that, you're nothing round here, I'm the boss and if I tell you to sit you'll sit, you'll sit until I say you can move – and I said to him (because I'd heard rumours, he never told me, but some of the other children must have said something – I can't remember – but I *knew*), I said to him, "I don't care what you do."' She lifts her eyes earnestly, candidly. '"I don't care what you do to me, I've got a white mother, and one day she'll come for me."' She speaks, passionately confident. 'I knew my mother would come for me, I *knew* she would – I never even remembered her, but I'd heard other children tell of her. My brother said, "*You!* You haven't got a white mother, you're a liar," and I said, "I have, and she'll come for me, and *you* won't matter any more," and he made me sit there all the longer because I cheeked him, but I didn't care.'

She lifts her suddenly eight-year-old eyes to me, earnest and innocent, and I suffer a crack in the chest, as though the tramping feet and the banners, all the miles and miles and miles of marches have been rolled up like so much old carpet in the face of this terrible candour, this amazing belief.

Unemployed – waiting, waiting, waiting. We talk in a desultory way about getting work, brood over the boards at the job centre, usually give up and go for coffee in Woolworth's. To be honest, neither of us 'deserves' a job, to use alien parlance, and this is freely admitted by both of us, laughing. We hardly ever go for jobs. The last one I went for, that I wanted, was at the social services department, on the switchboard. There were lots of other applicants being interviewed on the same day as me, so I wasn't so surprised not to get it. But the following week I went into the job centre, and the details were still on the board. It was exactly the same job, because I told one of the interviewers, and she rang through to check it. Since then, I've not bothered at all. Hawa once got sent for a shop job, but the pay was so low she was pleased not to get it.

'I mean, I didn't want to take the job away from somebody – somebody might really want it; I didn't want to take it off them.'

'How very considerate of you.' We laugh.

Hawa is wearing dark spectacles, because she thinks she might be being followed by two Somali men. 'Do I look silly wearing these at this time of year? But I'm sure . . . I can tell Somali men, even when they wear ordinary clothes. I'm sure I'm being followed . . .'

Our conversations – honestly, it's like entering the catacombs; we don't know where they will lead, we both ramble on, forgetting the story we started out with.

'I said to my mum, "Why ever did you marry my dad?" because she was only a teenager and he was in his sixties, and she gave up everything – her brothers wouldn't have anything to do with her, people called her in the streets, her mother wouldn't speak to her for years – not till she saw the children, and she real loved us when she saw us. That's my granny – ooooo, I love my granny, she's ever so little and ever so cute.

'I've got this English granny,' she explains seriously, as though it's quite a marvel, 'and when we go to see her, at New Year, she has a party for us, and she dances – you know, the way grannies dance, showing all her long knickers . . .'

The re-run of *Roots* is starting again on television, Hawa says. Would I like to go down and watch it with them? She is very excited, it's the best programme on television she has ever seen, and she and Teddy followed it every week the first time round.

Winter sets in. The house is cold, but the attic is freezing. I stand on the table to scatter bird seed on the window, and close it very gently, so it won't slide off. Then lots of tiny birds come, mostly sparrows, and from underneath I watch their warm moving little bodies, peering up, a couple of feet away from eager eyes. As I sit, trying to work, there is a tap-tapping on the glass as they pick up the seeds and bread with their beaks. In the mornings, after rising to make tea and breakfast and a fresh hot water bottle, I often go back to bed, because it is just so cold. Or I sit in the chair, cocooned inside my sleeping-bag like a bug, wrapped round with a blanket and clutching the bottle. The paraffin-heater takes ages to warm the room, and it is too expensive to have on day and night, except in the very fiercest cold, and after I've just got my Giro. It is that interesting winter when everybody except the miners has gone on strike, and there are some food shortages in the shops. I am glad I have no job and don't have to turn out in the mornings. I stay in bed until about ten o'clock. It is so cold the ink in my biros freezes too, and each morning I have to warm them in hot tea.

On Thursdays I go off at eight-thirty to a Red Cross class lasting all day, leaving a cold casserole in the oven, and at three o'clock Hawa switches on the oven, so the casserole will be ready for half-past five. In the really bitter cold I fill the paraffin can right to the top before I leave, and it burns all day, which is a waste, but it's better than spending the evening in an icy room after I've plodded home through the snow. Hawa looks in at midday, to make sure the heater is all right.

Three afternoons in the week she comes up to my eyrie under the roof, and we settle cosily round the heater and talk lazily about getting jobs but not yet. Hawa shows me her photographs, taken at her first modelling jobs. They don't do her justice; she maintains a haughty pose, looks as though for two pins she would kick the photographer in the teeth. She is really waiting to hear about her divorce. She has applied for it, but there are all sorts of complications, which I don't understand, and neither does she. In any case, she hasn't been in to see the solicitor recently.

On Wednesday evenings I pull my door to and trip down the two staircases to the ground floor, to watch their television. Teddy and Hawa's sitting-room is the biggest room in the house, and I sit looking round at the high ceiling with its plaster scrolls. A dark red plush prayer-mat with a picture of Mecca woven into it is hung over the black marble mantel on which is an assortment of ornaments, including a red rose in a glass globe and a big photograph of Hawa. Right across the main wall is an assegai spear, and a black wooden African mask is strung up behind a mass array of rubber plants and parlour palms. The mask has an unhappy expression, not as though it is dead, but dumb, as though it has been made speechless. A strange musky smell comes from the plants. In the big bay of the window, on view to the street outside, sit two carved wooden deer, one dark, one light. Each time the door is pulled open there is the slightest rippling from the dulled angel-chimes under the palms.

'What is the mask of?'

'It's a tribal mask. It's a cast taken from a real one. The spear – that's for real.' He talks quickly, maybe from nerves or maybe he doesn't really want me to understand too much of what he is saying. He lifts the spear from the wall gently, and hands it to me – I nearly drop it, it's so heavy. Teddy's shoulders shake with laughter, a dancing lemon glitter in his eyes.

We watch the television in total darkness, as if to be more reverential. After the first episode, the rest of it seems like an anti-climax to me, after that initial scream.

The light goes on, we blink. 'I don't understand how those

men could have done that – those men on the ships. They must have seen what they were doing.'

'It was *wickedness*,' steams Hawa.

Teddy, with his face bent low over his hands, protests mildly, sadly, 'But everybody's wicked.'

It is spring; I wake up now in the mornings with the noise of pigeons all around, bright light streaming through the glass. And the sound of the singing of birds is come. In the park the worms come out on to the paths to revel in the warm rain, thrashing about in ecstasies, and the air is full of the smell of limeflowers. Hawa gets made up, puts on her best clothes, and strolls into town to see the solicitor about the divorce.

Teddy has decided my table under the attic glass is ideal for starting off his cannabis seedlings.

It seems bad to be inside, without jobs and a task to go to; that there is nothing wanting you out there in the sunshine and the movement.

One day Hawa comes knocking on my door, spilling over with joy. 'My mother's coming. She's found out where I am. I knew she would, I knew she'd find me. I wanted to send her something – some money to help her out. But I didn't put an address on it.' Tears fill her eyes suddenly, and she turns bitter. 'But she only spends it all on the children. But that must be how she found out where I was. She must have seen the postmark and made enquiries amongst the Somali people. Those two men *were* following me.'

At the end of the week she and Teddy go into town to order a new suite on HP, to arrive before Hawa's mother.

'Miss Hal's mother here,' announces Mohammed, when he comes to collect the rent on the following Friday. On the landing Mr Sandman, the Old Man, just stands; he seems to know there is someone new in the house.

Hawa's mother stays a day and a night, then she returns to her family. Hawa is jubilant. 'My mum really got on with Teddy; she was interested in him, she asked him lots of questions, and she liked the room and the meals I cooked for her . . .'

When Hawa goes off to make the coffee Teddy's uncle

looks at him. He is a little, old guy. He has been here a long time.

'It was all right. She was all right. I liked her. I think she's getting used to the idea – me and Hal . . .'

Teddy's uncle half-smiles, and shakes his head, very very slowly.

'I don't believe one word you saying, man.' As it turned out, he was right.

About a month later, Teddy's family receives a telephone call for Hawa. Teddy's younger brother Tarrant comes knocking at the front door. By the time Hawa has put on her court shoes, patted her hair and blinked her lashes a few times in the bedroom mirror, and hurried back with Tarrant, the caller has rung off, not leaving a name but a message for Hawa to receive a call the following evening.

'It's my mother, I think. I know it's my mother . . .'

The next morning she comes into the kitchen whilst I'm cooking my breakfast, which is dead early for her.

'That phone call was from my mother. She's seen my husband, and she says he'll agree to a divorce without any fuss if I do as she wants. She wants me to go to Dubai for six months and, if I do, and I still want to come back to Teddy, they won't stand in my way, they'll accept it then. She says there's a job wait'n' for me, and my cousin Yvonne is out there now, and she'll look after me. I might, you know, I feel like a change, it's gett'n' me down, not having a job all the time. I've told Teddy – I can save whilst I'm over there, you can make pots of money there . . . God, I'd better go or Teddy'll get mad. He's not very pleased about it.'

In the daytimes the house is not normally noisy but after Hawa leaves it is totally silent on weekdays. Even on Thursday evenings, when Teddy used to celebrate pay-day by playing the stereo full blast, it is quiet. If I run to answer the bell Teddy splits open his door a fraction before I reach the front door and, showing half of a miserable eye, he mumbles, 'Tell them I'm not in.'

'He says he will wait one year. One year,' Mohammed emphasises stridently, laying one of his fingers in the air. 'After then, finish. Not wait.' He slices across with his two hands.

Teddy's sisters don't come so often, now that he doesn't answer the door; but nearly every day a young guy I don't know stands there, shoulders squared as though carrying a great deal of fury around with him. 'Is Ted in?' Eventually, I stop answering the bell too.

The end of Ramadan comes in late summer that year. Mohammed makes lots of stirrings in an enormous pot, and the little girls come round in their gold tinsel and pink and red, with *mendi* on their hands and lolly on their cheeks. Zarina is determined to adorn me too, and I yield up the palms of my hands. Tiny Shamuna, she of the red shoes, wears bracelets and a tinkling necklace, and all of her little fingers, with their bright red nails, clutch sticks of *ladoo*. Mohammed comes up and down the attic stairs with each different wriggling toppling baby that is brought to the house, lots and lots of them. Mr Sandman takes off on his bike, and isn't seen for weeks. Teddy doesn't appear for ages, either, and he misses going to work.

The next week, in between a buff envelope with my Giro and a postcard demanding library books be taken back, is a postcard, showing hotels and a turquoise sky. On the back it says 'It is very nice here. I am working in hotel on the side of the picture as receptionist. Love, Hawa.' I prop it on the wooden shelf of the dressing table, and hum as I make breakfast.

When he comes for the rent Mohammed peruses the postcard slowly and carefully, and then declares very definitely, 'She is a liar.' He sounds so convinced of this, that I stare at him. ' "It is nice here," ' he quotes slowly. Then, with considerable force, 'Is not nice there – you know what I mean? – chop off the hand, put out the eyes.' He makes gestures, cracking at his wrist with his other hand, poking a finger at his eyes. Then he shakes his head slowly and mournfully. I don't know what to say – it's just a holiday postcard, not a political analysis. That afternoon, almost straight from work, Teddy comes bounding up the small attic stairway to see the card. He reads it with a face eager and crestfallen at the same time. In a few days, a card comes for him too – naughty Hawa has posted it later, to make him squirm a little.

In the kitchen Teddy's soldering iron is propped on the

draining-board to cool – he has just been mending my wireless which stands with its back off, waiting to dry, I think. Teddy and I consult *The Book of Fate*: How is Hawa and what is she doing now? Will the traveller return safely? Will she I love prove faithful or treacherous?

Teddy makes marks on a piece of paper with a biro, and scores them off, whilst Mohammed laughs over his cooking pan and pours scorn on the enterprise.

'Miss Hal very beautiful. She not come back. Ha ha ha ha ha.'

The Book of Fate tells us 'Your friend is well and sleeps soundly. She is content and happy. The traveller will return richly laden.'

We can't read the answer to the final question, because that page is missing; I pulled it out one time in a temper, which probably means the answer wasn't very encouraging.

'It's missing, you'll have to ask again.'

Mohammed tucks a napkin into his collar, and sits down over his evening meal, eating heartily while Teddy is saddened, remembering the time when he grabbed his little piece of warm and shaking Africa, and ran.

He bends over the sheet of paper again, to produce the answer 'The heart which is filled with love for you will prove true.'

'Miss Hal not come back.'

'Stop telling him that, it's cruel,' I say, when Teddy takes his soldering equipment to the cupboard.

'Is not cruel,' Mohammed replies energetically. 'Is best.' He fills his vacuum flask, turns his tomatoes, which lie in ranks on the kitchen windowsill, waiting to blush up to the right degree of redness, and goes shuffling off to his shift. I whip down a pillowcase and some towels from the rack, and fade up the attic stairs, and Teddy, not much encouraged by *The Book of Fate*, goes off to listen to dub.

As the year rolled on the evenings darkened, and became lively with the noise of rockets and bangers, as children anticipated Bonfire Night and Diwali. It would be Hawa's twentieth birthday on Guy Fawkes Night, and I wondered how Teddy was keeping, for I hadn't seen him or heard him around for a couple of weeks, not since he had borrowed my *Radio Times*, and returned it on the day it expired. But I hadn't seen him, he had left it on the attic stairs. I thought I might knock (or should I?) on her birthday, as he might be feeling low.

It was Saturday night, and I slipped out to get a loaf and some sweets. But the November dark was too alive, and I took off down the street on the other side of the hill, and walked about until I saw flames. They were leaping from the back yard of what used to be a grocery shop, well stocked with provisions and always full of customers. But the corner doorway was bricked up now, blanked out. The biggest bonfire I'd ever seen blazed and flamed nearly to the top of the houses. The houses would be down soon, anyway. They looked miniature in the flames, the people still living in some of them floated worried faces at tiny upstairs back windows. There was a silence; only the sound of the fire gnawed and cracked round boxes and mattresses and discarded furniture. The people collected there seemed from the past, like people who had been at street bonfires a long time ago. With them, his face lanterned on to the night, I saw the Old Man from Mohammed's. He was standing very still, watching the life in the fire.

When I returned, closing the front door but leaving the inner door, as the Old Man was still out there somewhere, I noticed the light was on in the big front sitting-room, and there was a hum of voices. So Teddy had friends or relations round. I reached my room, and pulled off my hooded coat and scarf, releasing the smoky November smell in my hair. There was a knock. I could tell it was Mohammed, but it was Saturday and I had paid the rent the day before. Besides, it wasn't that sort of a knock.

'Miss Hal has come,' he said, smiling. 'She has come back. Teddy went to London to collect.' We nodded wonderingly at one another.

On Monday I saw her. She didn't seem to have changed much; she came towards me in the corridor in her bluey-haze *dirit* and said, 'Hi,' her dark eyes smoking.

Any slight inclination I had to get a job vanished with the warmth, and once more it was water-bottles and blankets and paraffin, a repeat of the previous winter. Hawa came up often in the afternoons again. She talked a lot about Somalia, and her childhood, the house, the land, her bad stepmother, the pet lamb she kept once, on a piece of rope.

'I never had toys, the only thing I ever remember was the lamb. My mother would have sent money for toys, I'm sure she would. I bet that old witch just took my mother's money and never gave me anything with it . . .' She said very little of her recent trip, except that she wanted to come back so much that they let her come before the agreed time was over. She talked more of her lamb, and ironed her blue *dirit*.

'I want you to have it. I want to give it to you,' she said, ironing French perfume into it. 'I expect we'll always always know each other,' she said, sealing her words with each press of the iron.

'It's lovely, but I like to see you wearing it.' I was pleased and sad as well.

More and more now, Teddy is only just the right side of antagonistic, if I bump into him. If Hawa slips out to the kitchen in the evening, when I've come down to make toast or heat soup, Teddy will come silently into the kitchen, wordlessly putting his hands on his hips, and looking daggers at Hawa, head dropped to one side. The talk or laughter ceases at once, silent consternation, as she whispers, 'I'd better go,' and I smile, turn my toast, stir my soup.

Hawa gets a job, modelling clothes in a department store.

'It's only for a week, but it's better than nothing. The money's rubbish, the *clothes* – I'm not kidd'n', the clothes are awful. Real dreary stuff. You even have to provide your own shoes and that. But it might be a start again, once I've done this job . . . Will you come and see me one afternoon?'

I've got a terrible problem, because (I don't know how it's happened) I seem to have got twenty-four overdue library books, and most of them seem to be big. Hawa agrees at once to help me take them into town. She picks up the nearest one, and staggers.

'My God, Carol, what's in this book? It must be something real clever.'

We turn the pages of *The Renaissance Engineers*. I can't understand a word.

'Do you mean to say,' she asks unbelievingly, 'you were reading this book because of a *man?*'

I nod. 'I can't understand it.' We both fall about laughing.

'You see – I wanted – I wanted,' I could hardly talk for laughing now, 'I wanted – to understand the way – the way – his mind worked.'

Hawa is very depressed. 'I'm going to get another letter from my mother, I know I am. She says they've accepted it, that I want to stay with Teddy, but I know they haven't. I expect I'll hear soon. I just know I will. They were angry with me for wanting to come back.' This is the first time she has really talked about her trip.

'My mother said, "How can you do this to your father, don't you know we want our children to get on, to *be* something, not just to be idling all their lives. Think of the sacrifices we've made . . ." It was worse for me as well because Abdul – that's my eldest brother – he didn't sit his exams; he drove round in my mum's car while the exams were going on, and then he came back and locked himself in his room. And my mum was crying and my dad went very quiet. Then my mother says, "All our children are letting us down. There's Abdul, we've been keeping him all this time . . . Jamad's just crashed somebody else's car . . . Djamila and Hassan," (that's the little ones) "they're getting just as naughty as the rest of you because of your example. You, my best one, living with a Jamaican." ' She breaks off. 'They think that's terrible. You can't argue with them.

'And then my mother says – she always says this when the children act up, because they blame this country, they think there's too much doing as you like here – she says, "Well, we're all going back to Africa. You children don't realise what shame it is for your father, with your bad ways . . . We're going back to Africa, and we're going to live decent lives, no more discos, no drinking . . ." '

'All families go through bad patches.'

'I suppose they do,' says Hawa, not at all cheered.

'Let's go to the park.' We collect our sandals and cardigans, and walk down Rosehill Street and into the arboretum. We sit on a bench, near one of the only two flowerbeds that are left. The sun doesn't lift Hawa, she is so low in spirits.

'Abu Dhabi – it was awful,' she says desperately. 'I didn't make any money – not one penny; I had to give everything I earned to Yvonne, as she'd paid for my ticket. I still never paid for it, and it was just a waste of money. Whenever bills came, I had to pay them, Yvonne kept being short and saying, "Has anybody got any money?" I never had any money, and I couldn't escape. I didn't know what to do. I did work a bit – not much, because over there you have to keep the house going and get food for when people arrive, otherwise it looks bad. And they're arriving all the time. Yvonne kept saying to me, trying to push me, "That's Unni, over there, he owns several hotels, go and be nice to him."' Hawa puts on a fancy scornful voice. '"And there's Abdi, he's very rich, he likes you, come along. This is Hawa, she's shy . . ." I hated it. I hated every minute of it.

'They all look down on Teddy. I mean, Teddy, he's quite good in lots of ways, he knows how kettles work . . .'

'Yes, and wirelesses.'

'But they don't care about that. To them, he's nothing.'

All around us fume wallflowers. Hawa is so unhappy, her face discontented, troubled, as we lean along the back of the form and stare into the wallflowers, smoking their scent into the air. A boy of about eleven cycles up.

'You in business?' he demands. We both turn and look back at him, and then ignore him.

'I was so unhappy. They were the worst months of my life,' Hawa says passionately. 'Yvonne made things as difficult as possible for me, all the time pretending to be helping me, showing me around. I just wanted to be back here, I didn't feel part of anything out there . . .'

The kid rides up again, crackling notes, and says even more truculently, 'I *said* – are you in business?'

'Push off. Go back to school.'

Hawa ignores him. 'All the time I was there – Teddy – he never lifted one finger to get me back.'

'I thought you had an agreement that it would be for six months.'

She doesn't bother answering this, just sweeps scorn into the air with her long lashes.

'He was very upset. And you didn't write to him.'

'What I'd like to do is to leave all of them – my mother – where she can't get at me; I mean – my family, Teddy. Teddy cares about me, I know he does, but I'm confused. He would have accepted it if I hadn't come back, it was all up to me,' she burns resentfully. 'He would never have come and got me. He just left me there,' she says bitterly.

It is probably time for her to go back, to cook their meal. We look up at the clock, but it is broken.

'I don't want to go back. I want to go away. I want to go away from *everywhere*,' says desperate Hawa.

At the end of that week I was away all weekend. On the following Monday I walked up from the station, humming a song to myself. The sun was warm on the streets which were awaiting demolition. They seemed to echo with emptiness, as many of the houses were tinned up. I moved past the house I grew up in, past Sassy's entry, past the house where the recent bonfire burned, which was now blackened and charred. At the top of the street, spread over the junction where four roads met, children played and called and dodged cars. Girls stood on the corner already. I passed the telephone box at the top of the street and, still humming, moving inside a tune, and waiting to kick off my high-heels as soon as I entered the house, I walked down the hill, swinging my bag. Down the street Hawa was out by the front gate, chatting to a man. My first thought was surprise – she was wearing jeans and a blue top which was exactly the same material as the blue dress I was wearing. I had never seen her in it before, and she couldn't have seen me wear the dress, because I'd only worn it once. I smiled and waved at her, partly at the coincidence, and she waved back, but half-heartedly, I thought. When I got nearer I saw the young man she was speaking to was a policeman in plain clothes. She drew slightly away from him, almost as though they had been sharing secrets, and he watched as I stopped and waited for him to move, so I could pass through the gate.

'Oh, do you come in here as well?' he asked, not antagonistically. 'How many more of you are there?' I smiled vaguely and looked at them both. Hawa didn't seem inclined to swap surprised glances at our identical wear.

'Do you know Todmore Bell?' he asked.

'Who?'

'He means Teddy,' said Hawa quietly.

'Yes, I know Teddy.'

'Could I ask you what you were doing on Friday night?'

'On Friday night . . . I was at the theatre in Nottingham. Why?'

He didn't answer. 'Who else lives here apart from you two and Todmore Bell?'

'Well, there's an old man, and the landlord.'

We both automatically looked up at the windows of Mohammed's room. He was hovering behind the nets, and disappeared when waved to come down. He appeared on the top step.

'Are you the landlord?'

Mohammed nodded yes.

'And do you know Todmore Bell, does he live here?'

Mohammed looked back at the policeman who then said, slowly and more loudly, *'Where were you on Friday night?'*

'Not here. Shift. Shift.'

'And you don't know Todmore Bell?'

'He means Teddy,' suddenly shrilled Hawa. 'There's been a rape and they think it's Teddy.'

'Now, I didn't say that,' said the policeman. Mohammed and I stared at the policeman as if he was mad.

'Teddy? Rape? Mr Teddy no rape.' Mohammed's speech, his meaning driven through an alien difficult tongue, always sounds as though he is labouring for the truth, and has the force and brevity of an oracle.

'So when do you expect him back then?'

'I don't know.'

'No idea.' Mohammed had already departed from the step, unwilling to waste more of his time. The truth was Teddy should have been back already. He must have got word not to come.

The policeman finally left. We moved through the hall to the kitchen, and Hawa switched off the flame under her saucepan.

'I think I'd better go round to his dad's and find out what's going off.'

I locked the vestibule door, and Hawa changed her top and pulled back her hair and left by the back of the house.

'Don't lock the gate Carol, I'll come back down the entry.'

The house stood silent. Both front and inner doors stayed

locked. The rooms at the front stayed dark; Hawa and Teddy retreated to their bedroom at the back. Nobody answered the door bell when it rang. It rang and rang. When that happened, all the lights went off at the back of the house too. Sometimes there were thunderings at the front, and one time when I had nipped out to the off-licence, I returned to see two policemen, their silver bits moving, their shapes all but merged into the evening. They stood inside the front gate, hammering at the door and leaning on the bell, and muttering at one another. I walked straight by the gate and down the street, and wandered about a bit, before slipping up the entry and tapping at the window.

Another time I was caught in the bathroom when the ringing started, so I moved silently down the long upstairs corridor. The Old Man had his door open and was just standing on the landing, looking. Behind him, the light in his room was switched off. Hawa was standing at the bottom of the stairs, looking up. None of us spoke. None of us ever discussed the fact that nobody answered the door.

I can understand Teddy's attitude – the police have a crime and they need to find a perpetrator. As long as they get somebody they are not so bothered about getting the person who did it. Teddy wasn't anxious that it should be him. He would probably rather they caught the guilty person or, failing that, somebody else. Not him. Therefore he was not putting himself in their way. I quite see his point.

The local police, what I've seen of them, could be worse. It depends what your expectations are, of course; they don't do much if you're burgled. You just have to put up with it. But any passing contact I've had with them, they have been moderately pleasant, and I still remember a local residents' action committee meeting to discuss demolition, which has the quaint distinction of being the only meeting I've been to where the audience was out-lefted by the police.

Whether the police got somebody for the rape, I never got to know. But anyway, in a week or two the house was back to normal: Teddy's hi-fi thumping out on Thursday nights, children coming and going at weekends, Mohammed's tape shrieking away in the dusk. Hawa said it was Teddy's cousin

Judas who rang the police and told them he had done the rape.

'They can't stand each other. They're the same age and they've never got on. There's always been jealousy between them.'

'What does Judas look like?'

'He's quite small, with a big Rasta hat. He always wears it. It's quite unusual, it's not knitted,' and I recognised the youth with the gloating expression, who kept coming round in the summer.

'We haven't seen him for ages. When Teddy first brought me he kept coming around and saying, "So you've found an African woman now." And he kept stopping me when I went to the shop. It didn't matter in the evenings; Teddy went then, but he was doing it in the day. Teddy had some days off work and watched me, and when he saw him stop me, he came up and they had a big row. He stopped doing it after that, but sometimes he used to just stand on the other corner *watching*, just so's I'd know he was there. He must've got fed up of this, because we heard he'd left and gone to another town.'

Then Hawa got a job, working in the Co-op cake factory.

'It's not much of a job, it's not what I want, but I'm sick of being inside, and I like it; I think when I wake up in the mornings: Well – I've got somewhere to go to today!'

I didn't see her much, she was too busy. One time she came and tapped on my door in the late afternoon, when she came from work.

'I wondered how you were – Teddy's gone to his sister's, so I thought I'd come and see you.'

She looked quite different, had acquired a decided way of moving, and swung a shoulder-bag and a black and white tartan concertina skirt, and the air seemed to spin around her as she moved.

But after a month, all of the girls were made redundant. They weren't told until the final pay-day. She came up to see me straight from work.

'I'm so fed up. Guess what's just happened – we've all been told not to come next week. Just as I was getting started again. I know it wasn't much of a job, but I'd got to like it, and I thought I was really good – I was getting up on time every day and going out. We've all just been for a drink, and we were all crying and that.' She laughs a little bit at this. 'Teddy – I'm not speaking to him. He's pleased about it, he said I was getting a dirty mouth, working at that place. Honestly. As soon as I seem to get on my feet, this happens.'

Lots of things happened that year, but nothing to change the shape of Hawa's life as she had changed it herself when she left home, and then left Abu Dhabi. We saw each other less often, and at the end of the year I moved to a place just round the corner, and she came to see me once a week. Then Teddy got notice he was being made redundant, so they moved from Mohammed's into a council flat a few streets away. When Teddy's redundancy money came through he bought a car, and Hawa became pregnant.

After they left Mohammed's I saw very little of her. Teddy was around in the daytime, and they often went out in the car. All of the hours in her day were spoken for; when I called there were always relations or friends there, and they all seemed to have lives encircled by husbands and children and certainties, and her life was part of that too, now.

Oddly enough, I called on the day she had the baby. The flats were very new, and I picked my way through lots of mud. There was nobody in but, just as I was leaving, a girl in an adjoining flat opened her door and said, 'Do you want Hal? She had the baby this morning, it's a little girl.'

I went into town and bought her some irises, which I knew she liked, and a dress for the baby, and left them with the neighbour. I hadn't seen her for months. It's when you don't see someone that the odd bitchy moments come to mind. Like the time Hawa told me her baby's African name, and I said the sort of thing you do say at such a time – that it sounded pretty, it couldn't be shortened, it was easy for English people to pronounce.

'I suppose it is. *Not* that I care about that,' she had said, looking at me with almighty contempt.

Yes and stuff you too, I thought, although actually I can see her point – why should she care? But I hadn't meant anything more than it was easy for most people to pronounce. If we had still been at Mohammed's, it would have been absorbed into everyday life, and neutralised by warmer exchanges. But we didn't meet for ages afterwards, so it left more of an effect.

Now and again – not very often – we bump into one another, usually in Sainsbury's. We talk about this and that – clothes, prices, general chit-chat. But it doesn't matter. We are still friends, and we'll be proper friends again at some time. I still have her hazey-blue, blue-grey, blue-pink *dirit*, and whilst I've been remembering her all this time it has been in here hanging up, an empty shape.

AT MOHAMMED'S

M OHAMMED'S HOUSE, A small villa in a terrace of villas, is set nearly half-way down the side of a hill, in a wide sloping street. At the top stands a telephone box, and the big back gate of the vicarage. At the bottom of the street is a small post office, across the road from The Duke of Cambridge, the public house much patronised by football fans before and after the match. It's only a few years since I lived there, but that time hangs now in my memory like a golden globe.

On the first day, I woke up on the big high bed, with my possessions piled up at the bottom, afloat on a still sea of old yellow and black lino. It was a square room, quite small, and full of curious angles in the ceiling, which was one half of the inclining roof. The bed was under the slope of the roof and window, which was great at night for looking at the stars and the night sky, but it meant my bed got wet when it rained and the window was left open. The only other thing in the room apart from the bed was the rickety three-legged dressing-table of pretty yellow wood, full of crannies and niches.

By standing on the bed I had a great view – chimneys and chimneys, a bit of the church, and a back garden where swarms of little Pakistani boys in Fair Isle pullovers climbed about all over the outside of their house, like the old woman who lived in a shoe's children did.

*

At the end of the first week, on a Friday evening, I am sitting in my room eating my tea, when a shuffling sounds outside on the small stairway, then comes a self-conscious cough, and a knock. I open the door. There is the landlord, Mohammed, swelling into the doorway, his beard rioting over his face, his big brows fierce. He scowls even more and extends a heavy plump palm in my direction, growling, '*Pay.*'

This makes me flutter a bit, although I realise what he means. 'The rent?' I stutter out, almost as though I am stalling. He nods slowly and weightily while, disconcerted, I fish about in my handbag, produce the agreed amount and place it on the still-waiting palm. The palm closes, he whisks straight out of the room, as though by magic.

The following Friday it happens just as before; he is very stern but not quite as fierce.

It is autumn, and very warm. I stroll about the streets and the arboretum, watching yellow leaves toss about.

At nights it is noisy; the wind howls round the rooftops and you notice it more in an attic; the doors shudder and rattle and the light bulb swings in the wind. Dogs rave at one another at periodic intervals throughout the night, and there is a sound I can't identify which resembles an old-fashioned steam train or an owl with a megaphone. There is a canine dawn chorus, and after that comes the church bell on Sundays. On Saturday afternoons in the autumn and winter comes the roar from the football ground, every time the local team score, and if I stand on the bottom of the bed I can see the floodlights, high into the sky.

The big bed is old – dirty and scrawled on, I mean, not antique and charming. It has bits of old chewing-gum and many scratchings and a message, 'Florence don't break the glass'. The bed and dressing-table must have stayed pushed up here for years, too heavy and too dilapidated to be worth moving. The dressing-table top is much scored and crayoned, and there are two tiny drawers for holding jewellery or handkerchiefs. In the middle of the modest pelmet at the top a child has scrawled her name: Maud. Not a child of today.

In the late hot autumn I put out the light and undress, watching sparks crackle into the dark. It is so high up here alongside the chimneys that sometimes I get scared I'll electrocute myself. If I can't sleep, I listen to the World Service in the middle of the night.

There are at least eight churches round here, a mosque, and a Sikh temple, across from which somebody has written in pink paint 'LUV GOD LUV NAYBOR OK'.

When I first came back to Rosehill I walked about in a daze of unbelief and curiosity. So much had changed. A three-foot high graffito in the town centre, celebrating the local football team, had had the letter P added to it by another scrawler, with horrific results: 'PRAMS RULE'. This seemed fitting, for I always seemed to be bumping into old schoolfriends; they walked about town with large demanding children, and husbands glued to their arms like barnacles, ready to pay the bills and take the responsibility.

At the end of the first month, the young feckless couple sharing a room on the first floor did a moonlight flit. They didn't owe any rent, but hadn't told anybody they were leaving. Nobody had seen them for over a week, and when Mohammed let himself into their room he found them gone and everything in place, nothing wrecked or stolen. The girl and Hawa used to have disagreements in the kitchen, but nothing very major, nothing that wouldn't have sorted itself out eventually.

'When you use – you must clean,' said Mohammed, in his kind but firm tone. The girl ran off back to their room with a howl.

'I'm sorry. She's a bit untidy,' said the youth, in a placatory sort of way. He was quite friendly and frequently seemed to be making excuses for her. 'I'm sorry – she is a terror when she gets into that bathroom: she won't come out.'

They had pale, plump, formless young faces, and that is all I can remember about them. Perhaps they felt so disapproved of that they just wanted to disappear. Anyway, the tenant who had the room next was the Old Man.

Hawa comes running upstairs to me, almost out of breath. 'Have you seen the new tenant?' she asks indignantly. I shake my head.

'It's a horrible dirty old bloke. I don't know where Mohammed found him. He must be desperate or something. He's wearing – like, rags.'

Naturally, I'm intrigued by this description, and keep a look out.

'Is that the new tenant?' Hawa glowers at Mohammed.

'He is very nice old man,' replies Mohammed, distant and definite, turning his back and going off.

'You want to keep your room locked, Serah,' she advises.

I meet the new tenant coming up towards me on the stairs. He is mild-looking and, it must be said – his clothes do look utterly filthy. The next day I see him in the kitchen, still wearing his overcoat, which is nearly to the ground. He has a small pan on the stove, and from the capacious overcoat he pushes out these big dirty fingers, with colossal grime-encrusted nails. He sees me looking at them, and draws them in again with a little smile, almost like shy pride.

'The leccy bill's come,' Hawa announces meaningfully, when I let myself into the hall. This will mean a row. It will be more intense at this time of year because it will be a winter bill. Bills always mean rows. I've never known a shared bill that hasn't caused someone not to feel hard done by at the way it has been split.

On Friday, after I have paid the rent, Mohammed tentatively pushes the newly-arrived bill at me. It is a tentative movement for the purposes of diplomacy only, for he is quite capable of going on to the vigorous offensive.

'What you think?'

'I don't know. Split it three ways?'

'Good idea,' he says jovially. 'Standing charge – they say – Mr Teddy – they will not pay.'

Hawa and Teddy dispute everything, down to the last detail. They pay eventually.

'If the standing charge isn't paid then nobody will get any electricity.'

'He's the landlord – he should pay it,' says Hawa. She collars Mohammed when he comes into the kitchen. 'What about that old man – why should he get off paying? He uses electricity.' Mohammed shakes his head. 'Yes he does, I bet he uses the electricity when nobody can see him . . .' she pursues relentlessly.

'He is old man, he does not use. Just a little, in hall, in kitchen sometimes,' answers Mohammed, mournfully indignant.

'He uses when nobody's looking, when we're all asleep at nights,' asserts Hawa.

'And he spies on people through his door, and the smell when he opens it . . .'

'He is very nice old man,' says Mohammed firmly. 'He comes, he goes, he bothers nobody. He will not pay.'

Eventually it is decided to split the standing charge four ways, including the Old Man, and the bill three ways, excluding him.

At first Hawa and Teddy regard me with deep suspicion, for agreeing with Mohammed over the standing charge and the Old Man. But recent events bring about a reversal in sympathies, when it suddenly occurs to me that the shillings which we feed into the bathroom meter in order to get hot water are repeated on the electricity bill, and therefore we have been paying twice. Hawa and Teddy are cock-a-hoop about this; it confirms their worst suspicions, that they are being cheated.

'No. Not shown.'

'Yes. It is shown. I asked the man from the Electricity Board.'

'Not shown.'

'Yes.' I take a reading of the meter, to wait for the next bill.

'We can understand that thing in the bathroom, and we know how much we've put in,' Hawa tells Mohammed.

'Oh very clever,' he replies, not meaning this at all.

When the next bill comes the two meter-readings are presented to him for deduction.

'It is not shown,' says Mohammed, labouring more than usual with his English on this important occasion. 'It is not shown on the bill.'

'It is on the bill, and I am not paying the bill unless you take off this amount.'

'All right,' says Mohammed cheerfully, not at all a bad loser.

Now and again Hawa and Teddy row between each other in the middle of the night; they come out on to the stairs shouting. Eventually Mohammed's lock will rattle as he turns his key, and he will go out too and shout at both of them, and then they argue a little bit with him too, before going back to their room.

I never know what any of the parties say, because it usually happens about three o'clock in the morning, and I'm in bed and sleepy, but can hear the tones of the voices, before turning over and going back to sleep.

At the top of the street – perhaps because it is on a hill – you can look down into amazing sunsets burning silently in the early evening sky, whilst waiting to use the telephone box, just after six. There is often a little crowd gathered there. On the other corner stand waiting girls – waiting for customers, or just somebody to talk to, perhaps to do a deal with, perhaps not. Often they are just chatting, in a casual, lively way.

A variant of casual pick-ups seems to operate on the corner telephone. Girls ring the number to see who will answer, and chat and sometimes make dates. So, when using the telephone, as you count your coins, you are quite likely to have it suddenly ring out at you, a sudden blast, trembling against the receiver as though itching to be picked up.

'Hello?'

'Oh, hello. Is there a boy there?' I look around. There's no boy.

'Sorry.'

'Are you sure?'

'Yes. Well . . . what boy, what's his name?'

Long pause. 'Errrrr . . . John.' I laugh. There is only one man waiting tonight – a tall Muslim who teaches the older boys at Saturday morning mosque, and he is plainly not John.

'No, there's no . . . oh, just a minute then, I'll ask.' I split open the kiosk door. 'Are you John?' I call, grinning. I was only having a little tease of him; I thought he'd be stuffy. But a slight smile appears; he looks at me as though I'm no better than I ought to be, which makes me laugh, and shakes his head in a smiling No.

At the moment I'm furious with Mohammed. I've just found out that none of our names are on the electoral roll, so none of us will be able to vote.

'I've got a bone to pick with you,' I say, going into the kitchen where Mohammed is cooking. He looks up.

'Why aren't our names on the electoral roll? When you filled in the form from the council, why didn't you put our names on too?'

'Form?'

'Yes. The form that came in the autumn, asking for everybody's name that lives in the house.'

He shakes his head. 'No form.'

'There was a form, because you filled it in with your name.'

He shakes his head again, slowly.

'You didn't put our names, and now we haven't got a vote.'

He says mildly, 'Not everyone wants to vote.'

'Not everyone wants to vote but they should be able to if they
want to. Because you didn't put our names we can't vote.'

'I put next time,' he answers, his serenity undisturbed. This
irritates me, that he doesn't realise how important it is, and how
furious I am.

'Next time – what good is that? We're none of us going to
be able to vote and it's a general election this year. It won't be
a general election next time. You must have deliberately filled
in your name and left ours off.'

'I fill in form, I am landlord, I put myself and my wife . . .'
he says, getting haughty.

'Your *wife* – your wife isn't bloody well here, is she? But
there are four other people in this house and you have taken
away their right to vote by sending in that form without their
names . . . The right to vote – everybody values that, people
have fought for that right . . .'

Mohammed watches, a big man with a smile slowly spreading
across his face, he watches as I stamp my foot and lose my
temper and give out a pretty little trill of democratic rhetoric, like
something small and decorative caught in the kitchen between
the pans and the knife.

'. . . it's not just a fancy word – democracy. If it isn't used
it will perish . . .' His phlegmatic acceptance of the loss of my
vote annoys and I stamp my foot again.

'You think because we don't have houses and cars and lots
of money that we shouldn't have a vote either. Well that doesn't
matter – we still have a vote. We're free. We have a vote. It
doesn't matter that we've got *nothing* – we still have a vote . . .'

Then suddenly he loses his temper too, a flash of scorn
crosses his face, a most unusual expression for him, and he
bursts out, 'Oh very proper English. Me – I am Pakistani, I
am funny man. You – very proper English.'

I am halted immediately and stand dumb.

'Oh, very proper English,' he says mockingly. 'Very proper English.'

Outraged, I fly upstairs and through the attic door, slamming it behind me. Once inside my room, I sit on the bed and start to cry.

Everything has changed, all the world; outside the whole country is voting and I can't vote. I can't understand how people's minds work and they can't understand me; I'm going to get old and mad . . . I sit counting up my woes to muffle the awful feeling that Mohammed thinks I think he is funny.

Well I don't care, I'm not stopping here, I'd like to go away to somewhere that doesn't exist and never come back. The tears pour out of me – I'm definitely going to leave.

There is a small knock on the door, really more of a scratch. I haven't heard any footsteps on the stair. I lift my head and quietly open the door. There is no one there. On the small square where the stairway comes to a stop is a bowl of golden rice, steaming away by itself. I pick it up at once, feeling spectacularly suddenly happy, like there's a rainbow streaming out of me, melting my tears. Mohammed must have stolen up – come a few steps and reached up and ledged the bowl at the top, before disappearing back down again.

The saffron rice tastes lovely: it's plumped with raisins and bits of nut and coconut.

The Old Man, Mr Sandman, is often seen from the main road, standing alone amid a rubble of houses like a sad chthonic visitant, small fires rippling at his feet. All about lie houses in ruins, a tangle of streets leading nowhere, starred with thistles, muddied diamond-patterned bricks undulating to the bottom of the hill.

Did he live here as a little boy? Nobody knows. If you ask him, he doesn't reply.

'Mr Vic – is he very very poor?' asks little Zarina anxiously. She is always extremely polite to him.

The Old Man isn't seen much in cold weather. His door stays firmly closed. Once, when his sister crossed town in the bitter weather to see him, he wouldn't even get out of bed to open the door.

'I can see him. I can see him,' and she stood there rattling his door-knob and calling. We each in turn bent and peered through the tiny keyhole.

'He's in there, and he won't even get out of bed to see me, and I've come all this way,' she wailed.

'Oh dear.'

'Get up, Vic, I can see you,' she called, losing her temper again and bashing at the door.

'Can't you let me in?' she implored.

'Me no have key,' replied Mohammed, discreet, non-commital. He shook his head and went away.

Once I saw in his room. I was on my way to the bathroom, and he was standing behind the door, chinked wide open, bent and watching through the wide crack. But watching so you could see he was watching, without any pretension of doing anything else. A fug of smoke and sleep drifted out on to the landing. I passed twice – to and from the bathroom – and, as I passed, looked in as though by accident. Inside there were torn pictures of nudes from men's magazines, and battered old Dinky cars piled at the bottom of the bed.

'Mahomet lets me . . .' he says, perhaps if he feels threatened. 'Mahomet says I can use the kitchen . . . Mahomet lets me keep my bike here.'

Now Mr Sandman is in trouble. He is in trouble with Social Security, and Mohammed isn't too pleased with him either. Apparently he cashed his Giro and straightaway took it round to a house where his friends were gathered. One of them took the whole amount from him and went off with it to the bookie's, to put on a horse. The horse lost.

'He's crashed it. He's crashed it. All my money. Whatever shall I do?'

He stands about in the corridor.

'You must go to labour exchange,' says Mohammed severely, and Teddy gives him an egg. He stands holding the egg and staring at it. Maybe a cooked egg seems like an impossibility to him just at the moment.

Eventually he goes to tell Social Security, and they call in the police. There is some dispute about whether or not Mr Sandman said the youth could place the money on a horse.

Naturally enough, the youth says he did, but Mr Sandman denies this. He stands denying it in the corridor, anxious to make it clear to everyone that it wasn't his responsibility.

Late in the summer in the house there is much decorating and cleaning going on. Mohammed's wife is coming from Pakistan. In honour of the occasion he papers the hallway and stairs, and his room, and a newspaper photograph has been pinned to the bathroom wall, of a man with centre-parted hair and a little moustache. Haven't a clue who it is.

On Saturday morning I go into the kitchen. Whilst I'm tinkering with food at the stove Mohammed appears in the curtained doorway. There is something strange about him. He looks struck: his eyes have gone liquid and very black, the pupils dilated. He speaks in a hoarse, awed whisper.

'My she has come.'

'I saw – *her* – last night in the kitchen,' Teddy says, slowly, quietly. 'Couldn't say a word to her. Not a thing. And yet . . . it's funny, I . . . felt I wanted to say something to her, somehow. I don't know why.'

In the autumn Mr Sandman is beaten up by youths. They take his money from him, and set fire to his cats. This is the first any of the tenants know he has cats.

The Old Man starts to cry. 'They threw beer all down my coat. I can't get it off, it's all over me . . .'

We look in great wonder at his coat, so utterly filthy, surely, that one more stain won't make any difference? But he is terribly upset. Actually, the coat is stinking. It was when he moved in nearly two years ago, and he is still wearing it.

'It's all over me. I can't get it out. I'll never get it out . . .'

In a way, I think I can understand. He is used to the way it smelt before, he got used to it, and now suddenly there is a whole new smell that he didn't want, and he hasn't had time to get used to it yet. He has built up his own and now it has been disturbed.

Two of us bathe his forehead; Mohammed stands looking mournful, raps on the glass of Teddy's door, and a long black arm comes out with a bottle of milk, and goes back in again. The police come.

A few days later he sees the mother-cat that he thought had been killed. At midday three of us go to the wasteground to collect her.

Standing among the bricks and confusion, the lines of concrete-mixers, the upturned land, I remember when these streets were alive with people, people whose lives were as real as the lives standing here now.

'Carol! Ca-a-a-arol . . .' shouts the voice of a dead friend. 'I'm not carrying your blinking hockey-stick, you can carry it yourself . . .' The walls have been wiped out, the roadway sliced across and ploughed into muddy furrows. Voices of children in the nearby school playground still float above the destruction.

This is where the Old Man comes to feed his cats; apparently, he has kept one of them on this ground for three years now. Overhead the sky, the clouds, they disintegrate and come together; it's like the clouds passing endlessly through my body, and I am sitting in one of the new flats to be built here, in Hawa's new kitchen, with her two-day-old baby squirming on my lap. Shell-frail skull, tiny claws of hands, opening and closing on nothing; face screwed up in its own dream.

'Do you remember how the Old Man used to stand on this ground, watching fires?'

'Oh yes,' but her voice drifts vaguely, she is still in the trance of birth.

'Oh yes – the Old Man.'

The following year Mr Sandman had a row with Mohammed – he wouldn't pay his rent, the cardinal sin, and he left. After that, whenever Hawa or I bumped into him in the street he said he was ill and was sleeping in a telephone box at nights. He was a lying old man, he was not sleeping in a telephone box. But he was plainly very ill. His neck had swollen right out, as though it had been pumped up all the way round, and his head hung more than usual because of it.

He was ill for a long time; he shuffled about town on his signing day with a piece of material wound about his monstrous neck. The last time I saw him, he seemed fine. He was smoking a pink Sobranie cigarette, and he said his father had just given him a red sports car.

'Oh. Lovely.' I didn't believe him. The cigarette was real, though.

'I like your posh fag.'

'Would you like one?' he said then, warmly, as though suddenly remembering his manners. This was the last time I saw him.

Although I always called him Mr Sandman, in my mind I thought of him as the Old Man. He was at Mohammed's for over two years, and when he left we knew very little more about him than we had when he arrived. He seemed not just old, but childlike.

'He is mental,' Mohammed would say, not in a condemning way, but as an excuse, a plea.

The Old Man would stand there with squared shoulders, waiting, waiting to see what you were going to do, going to say: waiting to see what blow fate would rain upon him next, maybe. Childlike, absurd, his stance telling out that he constituted no threat. A person in retreat. This simplifies matters for other people: it's non-taxing and easy to take in at a glance.

There was only one time I saw him when he didn't fit in with this self-created figure. Early on a Saturday morning I hurried out of my room and down the stairs. Mr Sandman stood smoking on the landing, in trousers and shirt, not the everlasting overcoat. His hair tousled, shirt open, it looked as if he was trying to get away from the smoke and accumulated memories in his room, as though he could bear them no longer. He raised his eyes to mine as I passed, like a total stranger. He looked mean, shifty, jaundiced, cynical. Just like any person who is down on their luck and has been down on their luck for most of their life. In that one dispassionate flicker of the eyes, as he raised them from looking at the floor, I saw something male and dishonoured, and cheated of life.

Triumphantly I twitch at the air before Mohammed with my voting card, '*See*. We can vote, we can vote.'

Mohammed laughs and stirs into his pot and says indulgently, 'Carol, you are mad, I think.'

'Hawa's got one too.'

Hawa looks at Mohammed with her special sizzling glance,

ostentatiously opens her handbag and pushes in her voting card, then we clatter off down the corridor and into the street.

'Don't forget – you can vote,' I call to Mr Sandman, who has come to stand unspeaking, watching. He has his Dinky cars and fold-outs from *Playboy*, and now he has a vote too.

When we get round the corner I cross the road, but Hawa stays put. 'It's over here, the polling-station,' I wave at her, but she stands there, so I cross back.

'Vote'n'?' asks Hawa, quizzical and amused. 'I'm not vote'n'.'

This bemuses me. 'Well . . . now you've got a vote, you may as well use it.'

'No.' She shakes her head scornfully. 'It's nothing to do with me.'

'It's only a school – come on. You only have to put a cross on a piece of paper.'

Hawa relentlessly shakes her head. She doesn't even bother to protest that she doesn't know who to vote for.

'Just come into the polling-station with me then, while I vote.'

She moves her head from side to side, adamant. I see she regards it as being like Teddy's sisters, Allison and Honesty, trying to get her to go into church, trying to inveigle her into something she doesn't understand. She just won't. She watches with an airy amused smile, slowly grinding her high-heel into the pavement as I cross the road and go past the railings of the school.

'You know, my mother voted once,' says Hawa, in raconteur mood, now that we are safely in town and away from the polling-station. She speaks as though it was quite an event. 'I don't know who it was, but she liked him; she reckoned he'd done someth'n' for her. An old guy with a pipe, he was, he come from Liverpool. She only voted the once. I remember that.'

'Why don't you vote, then? You could write and tell her,' I say, half-facetiously.

She shines back at me. She is not voting.

'Why,' I ask then, 'were you so mad at Mohammed, if you don't want to vote? I mean, what does it matter? Why the fuss when he didn't put your name on the electoral roll?'

'You made the fuss about that,' she points out. 'But I was

mad too. Him wiping our names off and that, like he was try'n'
to make out we never existed . . .'

Outside in the garden Mohammed is standing straight and
still, while at his feet his new wife grubs about with her head
near the ground, planting vegetables. He has one hand imperially
leaning on a spade, and a big satisfied smirk on his face. I could
just go out and pull his ears.

That spring, I go out leaving the attic window propped open
with the chair leg, as usual. There is a downpour, and I return
to find the room soaking and the light bulb immediately under
the window dripping and winking on and off alarmingly. Then
all the lights in the house go off.

One by one, doors open and faces peer out. Mohammed
is banged up from his rightful sleep, and he goes lumbering
off down the cellar with a torch. I follow him down in the
whitewashed murk full of webby crannies, the floor still dusty
with the coal which used to be kept down here. He fiddles about
inside the fusebox for a while, slotting the old china pieces in and
out and examining them. Above are the whitewashed rafters of
the floor above, and the whole house, pressing down, waiting
while Mohammed puts right what was wrong.

'You go – upstairs,' says Mohammed.

'Shall I hold the torch?'

'All right.' He hands it over, and shakes his head. 'This –
not good.' Above, unseen, the household waits.

'Is it a fuse that's blown?' I ask, trying to appear half-way
intelligent.

He pulls down the corners of his mouth in denial. 'This time,
no. I fix for now. But not good.'

'How do you know how to mend this; who taught you?' I wait
for an answer while he twists wire.

'I know. I learn from man.' He taps his head. 'I learn. I watch.'

He does drive people mad when they come to lay carpet or
mend the chimney. He stands watching them. 'They won't like
it if you stand watching them,' I told him once.

'I pay. I watch.'

The two men laying the staircarpet got quite nasty. (But what
Mohammed was doing was watching closely so that next time
he could do it for himself.)

'How long have you lived here?'

'I come, age fifteen.'

So he must have completely missed his schooling and gone straight to work, learning enough English to get to work and do his job. He can mend nearly everything, and at work he is now a crane-driver. He is clever, I think. With his two hands and a great faith in the future he has made his life. For years and years he has sustained other people, looked after his relations, fulfilled his duties. He is a very good man. He is a man you can trust.

I have a lovely memory of Mohammed. It was the afternoon of Christmas Eve, and I had left his house three weeks before. I was returning from town, and walking down the street was Mohammed, with his arms full of toddlers, Imran on his back, small Shamuna running ahead, clutching a parcel. They came in, the infants' eyes rounding more and more at the paper garlands, and then they went squealing off in all directions, chasing cats. They seemed particularly taken with a hanging bunch of balloons, so when they left I detached the thread and handed it to Mohammed, poking it in among the children he held.

The opposite side of the street was demolished, and a fierce wind whipped down the road. Just as the merry party was about to turn and head home, a great gust of wind howled down the road and detached the balloons, one by one, from the cotton, and they floated free.

'Ohhhhhh,' said all the babies in a collective sigh, a little noise of disappointment and wonder; their heads turned and all their longing eyes followed the balloons as they danced free. A passer-by laughed as Shamuna and I sped down the road, snatching after them with shrieks. Mohammed, his great arms full of other people's children, stood and shook with laughter; the yellow and red and orange globes whirled away on the escaping wind, and the babies shook too as Mohammed laughed and laughed.

The school holidays have started. As it happens, that summer I see quite a lot of Zarina and her little sister, as their mother has gone to Pakistan to visit her relations, so the children seem to have more spare time than usual.

Zarina is nine; she is pleasant and interesting company, but Shamuna, a small tinsel-clad infant who can understand English but speaks only Punjabi, has the trying habit of suddenly casting herself to the floor and howling out her woes. Zarina, meanwhile, folds her hands together primly and invites those present to voice their disapproval.

'She's naughty, isn't she? She's saying now that she's going to scream until you give her what she wants. Isn't she naughty? I didn't use to be like that.'

Zarina labours to show me how to do cursive writing, which is how they all write at juniors now, and teaches me some Punjabi words for simple things like dog and cat and orange. She is a very stern little teacher.

'No, *no – sirb. Sirb,*' she scolds after I've said sorb (for apple) for the umpteenth time. When she gets bored she nags for stories about Muezza, Mohammed's favourite cat. Knowing nothing about her, I make it up. Later, Ahmed claims to have found out she is a coal-black cat who sleeps inside the Prophet's sleeve. But I've knitted her in grey and black wool, knit a row, purl a row, so Muezza is fixed firmly in my mind as a tabby.

Zarina comes round one afternoon, moping because *Snow White* is on at the pictures, and she can't go to see it. Snow White is a great favourite with her.

'What about Cinderella?' I ask, as a tease, for I know very well she isn't keen on Cinders. She makes a little face in reply.

'I always liked the Ugly Sisters. The Prince would have had more fun if he'd married one of them.'

'*I* don't like the Ugly Sisters! They're ugly,' she says indignantly.

'Well, who did you like, then, who was your favourite? Dandini?'

'I don't know, I can't remember that one. Buttons. I quite liked Buttons. I liked Buttons better than Cinderella. No – I liked the Fairy best.'

'What was she like?'

'She had this pretty dress and curls and a little tiddly crown. And a wand with a star on the end.'

'Was she the Sugar Plum Fairy?'

'Mmmmmm . . . n-n-nooooooooo, I don't believe she was,'

answers Zarina, in the slow measured tones of one carefully sifting the evidence.

Like Zarina, when I was small I liked Snow White. She was the only dark heroine in the fairy tales I knew. She was dark and I was dark. A child as white as snow, as black as ebony, as red as blood. A magic child.

'What about Sita – she runs to the woods like Snow White, and she's the most beautiful in the world, Carol – she has a face like the sun and the moon.'

'Gosh. Do they have a pantomime of Rama and Sita? I saw children's paintings of it in the school, when I went to vote.'

'I'm not sure.'

'Well, if it ever comes round as a pantomime, you can take me.'

Zarina stares back, greatly amused. 'Oh, all right then,' she answers goodnaturedly.

'Where did the drawfs come from, who were they?'

'Dwar – they were miners . . .'

'Dwarfs? Are you sure?' I nod. 'Did Snow White have a little house? I've seen a little house in pictures.'

'It was the dwarfs' house. It was in a wood. She kept house for the dwarfs when they went off to work; she did the cleaning and made pastry and . . .'

'Ohhhhhh . . .' spurts up Zarina on a sudden geyser of passion. 'Oh Carol, please *please* can we make pastry just like Snow White?'

Oh Lord. I make pastry about once a year, and I do it by going to Sainsbury's and buying a packet of the frozen kind and hanging around until it has thawed. However, a pair of hopeful eyes is fixed upon me.

'I don't see how we can make pastry *just* like Snow White. She had birds helping her, as I remember. We could make drizzle cake, if you like.' There is a sponge mix in my dressing-table drawer, so it should work. We climb the two staircases to the top of the house.

Mohammed comes to tell the news. He is looking red-eyed and sad.

'That bloody fucking barstid Zia – he has killed poor Mr Bhutto.'

'Oh dear. I'm sorry. They have done it, then.'

He nods sorrowfully. 'Poor Mr Bhutto. That Zia, he is a very bad man.'

He goes off with bent head, and isn't around in the house for several days, so I think there is much to-do about it in the community. The photograph in the bathroom has disappeared.

'The Fair's coming,' Zarina rushes round to tell me. Her mother is still in Pakistan, so I take her and Shamuna on the Thursday.

After the long walk to the fairground, we head straight into the noise and the mud, the hoop-la, coconut shy, dodgems and the painted bounding horses. We win beads and sweets, and an 'I HATE JR' badge. Shamuna gets a small teddy-bear, which she keeps holding level with her face and kissing ecstatically. Later on, we have to pull her away, howling and growling, from assaulting a small Irishman. He stands, wearing a tiny papier-mâché Homberg with its elastic pulled under his chin, looking down at her benevolently as she yells and reaches up to thump his stomach, which swells under his blue Aertex shirt and braces, and is caught in his trousers like a plump acorn in its cup.

By the time we leave the fairground we look thoroughly disreputable: the quilted bottoms of Zarina's pyjamas are covered in mud, my hair has escaped its grips, Shamuna has lost a shoe in the mud.

'She says she doesn't care. *Isn't* she naughty?' Shamuna gives out a low chuckle, and kisses her bear. We sing 'Ten Green Bottles', and after that Zarina gives us 'Bobby Shaftoe', complete with handclaps.

The moon comes up behind the housetops as we walk home:

> The moon shines bright on Charlie Chaplin,
> His boots are cracking, his boots are cracking,
> Oh, the moon shines bright on Charlie Chaplin,
> Until they send him to the Dardanelles.

We sing our way home; the moon rises up at the end of the street, shining straight into our path, big and silver and very close to the earth.

The following Sunday afternoon there is a knock on my door. It is Hawa. She comes in, showing her bruised face where she has been knocked about. She took Allison to the Fair on the Saturday, and got beaten up.

'It was a gang of girls. They all kept shouting, "Look at her – who does she think she is? She really thinks she's somebody," and stuff like that. I hit them back, but it was all of them against me and I couldn't get away because of my high-heels. They ripped my dress – I did hit them back.' She keeps saying this, anxious to make it clear. 'I was worried for Allison – being so tall she looks older than eleven. But they didn't touch her. I was kicking at them, but they still got me. I didn't know any of them. I'd never seen them before. One of them says, "Oh *look*, you've torn your dress." Allison waited for me and picked my things up and we came home. You should have seen me – my clothes were all torn and one of my heels was broken. I felt a right tramp.'

'Honestly, I really suffer because of my looks. Teddy gets mad when people stare at me, and girls don't like it. Now this!'

I make a drink, and she talks on, about her life, about her hopes.

'I don't care if people don't like it, I want to *be* somebody; I like to dress up nice and to feel I'm going somewhere, not just to be scruffy. I want for me and Teddy to get on.

'You know,' she says, tipping her head to one side, 'being cut – it doesn't make any difference to me. If they do it to spoil things for us – well, they're wrong. They're wrong.'

As she speaks, the light falls down from the attic window on her dark curls. Her words, or the way the light falls streaming upon her, or being in this room with its old furniture – whatever the reason, she speaks the words of a mutilated Edwardian girl mentioned by Havelock Ellis. 'He thinks he's spoiled my pleasure. But he's wrong.' This was spoken so long ago, so long ago, and the ring of triumph is still there, carried over the years, insubstantial as a fragrance. Oh Florence, don't break the glass . . .

I remember the first Christmas Eve at Mohammed's. The house stood silent; I was in bed when the bell from St James's church started up. The attic, with its small litter of Christmas cards and packets of biscuits on the dressing-table, the pot of holly, the scrawl of past children's names on the furniture, all seemed held inside the vibration of the bell. I hadn't been inside a church for years, but suddenly took it into my mind to go. After a while the bell started tolling in a different, slower way, to indicate the service would soon begin. I hurried on my skirt and coat, and ran out.

Pushing the big gate, which for years had the unofficial scrawl 'Krsna' in mauve paint, I reached the church porch. The bell had stopped, and I nearly turned back. But I moved the heavy iron hoop handle round as carefully and quietly as possible, remembering when I used to come here late for school services and had to catch my breath for quiet. The door moved, and I passed through the doorway I had only ever entered as a child, turning to lodge the latch back.

The service had started, and I waited while the procession of choristers and clergy made its way to the front, the brass cross held high, and the choir, large and small, moving slowly and swinging censers. All lights were at the front, in the choir stalls and on the pulpit, and I hovered at the back in the gloom, waiting for the singers to finish their tread to the altar. About the stone pillars were wreaths of fresh fir and ivy, and a large Christmas tree stood next to the font and the silent dark figures of the crib. In the shadows, surrounded by unlit tapers, I made out the shapes of the oxen, Joseph with his staff, stooping Mary, a sheaf of straw . . . My God! The Baby was gone! It wasn't there! I felt a creeping feeling all over. I looked at the singing people, at the lights darting about on the travelling cross, at the gowned and cassocked procession swinging and swaying up the aisle. None of them knew the Baby had gone. I must have been seeing things; it must be there. I looked again at the crib, to see if my eyes had made a mistake in the gloom when I had first come in. No. There was no Baby. Just an empty hollow of straw. The blood burned in my face as I moved into a pew.

At the front stood the vicar. 'Beloved in Christ, we are gathered together to hear again the message of the angels . . .'

I felt sick. Whatever would happen, after all the praying, when the whole church went singing to the manger and found there was no Baby? The service had only just begun and it was going to go on and on, and all the time . . . It was like a nightmare, relieved only minimally when a couple of stragglers came in late. Perhaps the vicar would think they had taken it. But he had seen me lurking at the back. Would he think I had taken it? The latecomers had had as much chance to take it as I had. But the way the vicar was looking at me – he seemed to think I was the culprit.

As we sang, it seemed like a dream. I must have got it wrong; it must have been there. But I knew I hadn't. In a distant and almost uninterested way my mind registered things remembered from schooldays – the lectern, the small marble Christ as shepherd in the children's corner; and the changes – the arched dome behind Father Masham was now celestial blue.

The pews filed out and the congregation and choir stood about the manger singing 'Hark the Herald Angels Sing', and the Baby was there. I felt sick again, after the relief of it. I still thought there had been a trick, or maybe a cover-up involved. They still probably thought I was guilty in some way, and now I wouldn't even have a chance to defend myself.

Then it was my turn to shake Father Masham's hand at the church door. His eyes looked knowing; he smiled a spiky triumphant smile, and my face burned when he wished me Happy Christmas.

When I returned, the house was still, and I walked up the two flights of stairs slowly, relieved and exhausted. It was all over. None of the people here knew what had just happened; they were all sleeping now, it was separate from them, they had their own problems, and none of them would have thought anything of it anyway.

THE SISTERS

AHMED COMES. HE comes beaming in in his red and gold leather slippers, looking as though he has just skimmed across the skies to get here.

'Did you want any errands?' He pulls off his parka and establishes himself in a chair, and I go to the kitchen to make a drink. As I return, we hear the letterbox crash.

'The door – there's someone at the door,' he says, excited at the idea of maybe a new person. But it's only the local free newspaper coming through. He seizes it, waves it about, and drops again into the chair, reading. 'Look. It's one of those sisters.'

I peer across at the main picture. It's of an old lady, standing on a doorstep and shaking her fist, presumably at the photographer. 'Miss Hester Woodleigh in defiant mood' the caption underneath reads.

'Those sisters. I know about those sisters, I heard somebody in a shop say to an old lady, "Are you one of those sisters?" They won't move out of their house.'

It's true. The council has been trying to get them out for years, but they just stay put. All around the streets have been razed; from one main road to another it looks like the Somme, but the sisters stay put.

'I can remember them from way back. They're twins, I think.'

'Twins?' repeats Ahmed unbelievingly. 'But twins are young.'

'Yes, and after that they're old. I know – we'll make some fudge and you can take it round to them.'

'Why should I take it?' he squeaks indignantly.

'Because you're small.' This sounds as though I'm going to send him in through the larder window.

'I'll take it on one condition,' he stipulates, a big Cheshire-cat grin appearing, 'that I can have some of the fudge.'

'This kitchen looks a mess,' he says sternly as we move into it. 'When my mother cooks she clears up straightaway.'

'If you've come to nag you can go straight back home again.'

He stands with waiting spoon while I weigh sugar and margarine into a pan and add evaporated milk. '*Custard*. You never make custard now, Carol. When are you ever going to make it again? I liked it when you made that vanilla custard. *And* blancmange. After I got beat up that time. And my mum was making me soup every day,' he enthuses nostalgically, 'and my big uncle sent me a postal order.'

He got beaten up last summer, when he was nine, by a gang of teenage boys. His face swelled out and one eye closed up, and his lips went purple and swollen. He puts the spoon down and sifts about in a drawer, pulling out a hand-mirror, regarding himself closely in it.

'Did I look ever so horrible after I got beat up?'

'Absolutely horrible.' He grins at me, then turns and scowls into the mirror, pulling a menacing face.

'I want to stir it.' I relinquish the spoon, and he stirs about whilst I grease a tin and put it ready.

'My dad doesn't like sweet things; he can't stand them. It's with running the kebab house, he's used only to meaty things. And some old men, you know, standing on street corners, they say, "Why should he give himself airs? He is only the shoemaker's son."'

'You pinched that out of a fairy tale.'

Ahmed giggles. 'I know.' Then he turns serious. 'But he is the shoemaker's son.'

'Just a minute. Let me add some more milk.'

'In Pakistan I have my own cow. She's called Tchiji, and she wears a bell. She knows my voice; she comes to me. I haven't seen her for a long time, not since I was four. I'll see her when we go back for a holiday. Next year, could be.' He says this every year.

'Will she still be there?'

'Yes,' he pipes, with heartrending faith, 'she's mine.'

'Stir it in the middle or it will stick to the pan.'

'Carol, have you ever seen a dinosaur dropping?' I don't think anybody has ever asked me this before. 'Our teacher's going to bring a plaster-cast of one to school.'

'Now that you mention it, we used to have them come round, a while back. About two hundred million years. I was small then. It was tropical round here. All up Rosehill Street was palm trees and there were no houses and lots of dinosaurs. And lots of sludge. Just hot sludge, going zu-uu-up zu-uu-u-up.'

'Zu-uu-up zu-uu-u-up,' he repeats. We gaze into the fudge. It's popping but it isn't going zu-uu-up zu-uu-u-up.

'There's a well in Rosehill Street. The council keep on at these people to fill it in, but they're not going to. Wells can be very useful.' Then he chants 'Out of the strong came forth sweetness', reading the syrup tin. 'That's a Samson, isn't it?'

'Is it? I don't know.'

'I think so. We did Samson at Sunday school.

'Oh yes, which one was that?'

'The one on the corner with the brick flowers. I went there when I was seven, when I was friends with this boy.' Ahmed goes to mosque every week, but he has been to most of the churches and Sunday schools round here. He likes to look around. The fudge boils over. I turn off the gas-flame and pour the liquid into the tin.

The fudge safely lodged in the fridge, we sit down with cups of tea.

'Tcheegee – what does that mean?'

'*Tchiji*. It means sweeties, it's what you give to little children to make them be happy and stop crying – Ah, don't cry, come have some *tchiji*.'

'Tcheegee,' I mutter back.

'*Tchiji*,' coaches Ahmed. 'And Pakistan, it's lovely, it's . . .' Words fail him, for once. He doesn't really seem to remember it much, but anyway it was better than here. Well, here was better than here, how it used to be.

'I think you ought to come with me to this place. It'll do you good, it'll be a nice walk.' It won't be a nice walk, it will be very muddy if we go the short way. 'Look, Ahmed – you wanted to go an errand, and now I'm sending you on one and you want me to come as well. That's no sort of errand. In any case,' I say cunningly, 'those sisters would be able to tell you what St Andrew's was like inside.' He can't see St Andrew's church, because it is down now.

'Every house you've lived in that I ask you about, you always say the same old thing – it's down.'

'Well, it usually is.'

'*And* the church as well!'

Once more we get out the old parish magazine with the picture of the church on it, and Ahmed fingers the pieces of coloured glass picked from the ruins.

'Those sisters went to St Andrew's. The Misses Woodleigh. They taught the babies' class on Sunday afternoons, and Miss Emily came every week in this very fancy hat. She used to play the piano, and they both used to smile a lot, I suppose because they taught the very tiny children.'

We prepare to leave. The fudge is still quite soft and so in its tin, packed about with greaseproof paper. I wind round a scarf, and Ahmed feels for the spell on his arm and adjusts it, a gesture automatic and unconscious, like small boys use to pull up their winter socks. The spell has got a bit raggy: he's been to the school baths in it.

The front door slams behind us, and we walk briskly along the crowded Saturday streets, turning away from the shops and down a small cobbled street and into the arboretum. In the afternoon the light is grey and bleak, the grass looks faded; the fountain has been still for many years now. We curve round its railinged side, staring gloomily into the dark pond whose floating vegetation is abloom with Coke bottles and paper cups glowing white in the dim afternoon. There are few people about on this cold day.

In the distance, on a hill, a man walks a dog. A boy cycles past us silently. All about, trees craze black lines into the winter sky, and above the arcade the clock shows the same time that it showed fifteen, twenty years ago – five to three.

I wonder about the afternoon when it stopped, imagine it as a summer afternoon, the grass strewn over with people, bright flowerbeds, a band playing, or rock-and-roll records, and people eating ice-creams. Nobody notices, but way above the clock has stopped. Always in the winter I imagine it to have stopped on a summer's day. In the summer I don't notice the clock at all. There is something uncanny about this same time all the time, like you're walking through a dream but the truth, as though a clock showing that time changes would be a lie.

We pass through the arcade into a small street and across the main road, descending into an area of mud stretching down to the next main road. A small cluster of new flats clings to the road. Streets and streets have been wiped out, thousands of homes, houses with their own gardens, little trees, privacy. Mud, pools of dried concrete, the beginnings of a carpark – the whole area is laid bare, the fall of the land exposed. The lower main road is windy and filthy with paper rubbish. St Andrew's House, a new Social Security office, dispensing Giros, not bread and wine, stands where the church once stood. We stand before it, maybe hoping for something to happen. Now the houses are down a fierce wind blasts through the road, claps papers, tosses my hair, makes Ahmed's pyjama trousers flap. He clutches his parka about him, and makes off with the fudge. I wait by the endless wall of the Social Security office. Over the road is the sisters' house, once just another house in a terrace, part of streets of terraced houses. Now it stands stark, the doorstep is well scrubbed, the dormer-window reflects the fading light; it is more remarkable than anything in sight. When Miss Hester stands at her doorway, what does she see? Does she wipe away the ruins as she looks?

Just as the lights go on all along the road, I see a little shape speeding towards me. 'Is it all right?'

'Yes. I gave them the fudge and they said thank you and they liked it.'

'Goody, was it Miss Hester or Miss Emily?'

'Both of them,' he says lavishly. 'And they were very nice; they asked me in. There was a piano in the room, a big one, and it had lilies standing on the top.'

'Lilies?' It is December. Artificial lilies, obviously.

'And one of them said she could remember you, and the other gave me a piece of cake. They said they'd always lived there, and they jolly well weren't going to move just for the old council.' We look at one another, greatly satisfied.

'And there were books there, and they have an eagle.'

'An eagle?' I sniff the air suspiciously. 'What do you mean, an eagle?'

'No, not an eagle. An eagle in a picture. A picture of an eagle. On the wall.'

We walk along the darkening road, noisy with traffic departing from the town.

'And Miss Emily, I liked her, she was kind to me, she smelt nice, she smelt of lavender, and she wore a sort of hat, a grey hat . . .'

'What?'

He withers mid-sentence. 'No, she hadn't got a hat – not on her head – the hat was on a peg.'

We walk silently now, along the road under the plane trees. When we are nearly in town Ahmed says, 'Carol?'

I stop stock still and say grimly, 'Yes?'

He swivels his head upwards. 'I never went.' I glare at him. 'I banged on the door and put the fudge on the doorstep and ran off. I thought they might be fierce.'

I glare some more. After a while he says, 'They could have had a big dog.'

We have turned into town, and stand on the bridge, looking down into the darkness. Across the water stands the lighted cathedral, and the Co-op cow burns red above the town. The weir spills over relentlessly, enough to wear you out watching it.

'It didn't use to be here,' reminisces Ahmed, 'when everything went zu-uu-up zu-uu-u-up.' We laugh. We laugh more and more.

'Come on. Let's go and get some tcheegee.'

'*Tchiji.*'

'*Tchiji.*'

We wander back up the wide hill to our part of the town. It's Saturday, and Ahmed's mother is waiting to cook his favourite meal – or maybe she isn't – and he hurries off into the night. Rosehill Street is alive with noise and activity; in the new evening the scent of fresh curry floats from the restaurants on the main road. I turn down a side-street and make my way home, wondering how Ahmed knew Miss Emily wore lavender-water, because I hadn't told him. I'd forgotten it. He said her hat was grey, and it was grey.

I didn't go to see those sisters. I don't know why. I wanted to. And Ahmed, he thought they might be fierce. Miss Hester, waving her fist. 'Miss Hester Woodleigh in defiant mood.' But I remember them smiling, remember the doves and pigeons that nested in the roof of the old church school; the sweet rotting smell that emanated from the old walls as the wall-heaters burnt into them, it still lingers. I can see Miss Hester smiling, leading forth the singing infants, and Miss Emily, in her pretty hat, playing the battered piano, wind gusting down the chimneys of the empty fireplaces that were big enough to stand in, and all of us singing:

> O that I had wings of angels
> Here to spread and heavenward fly,
> I would seek the gates of Sion
> Far beyond the starry sky.

ROUND THE FIRE

ALTHOUGH MUCH OF the snow has melted the weather is bitter cold, and one Sunday Ahmed and I sit by the fire in the late afternoon with mugs of thick sweet cocoa, toasting bread and laying margarine and honey across it.

'Mmmmmm, I love stripy toast. It's the best toast,' he says, holding out the slice of bread on a fork before the sighing gas-fire, behind its bars. I fetch a packet of gingernuts from the kitchen.

'Are we in the parlour?' asks Ahmed, looking at the piles of bread and the pot of honey.

'The . . . Oh, yes, I suppose we are. We're not in the counting-house, that's for sure. Have a gingernut.'

He crackles around in the packet. 'My granny doesn't like gingernuts. She says they hurt her teeth.'

'How is your granny – is she settling down now?' Ahmed's granny wasn't well, so she came to England to be with her sons, so they could look after her. As soon as she was well enough to walk about, she was taken on her first visit into town, and shown the mummy in the museum.

'She's well. She misses Pakistan, but she likes it here. She and my grandad, they used to have this horse, it was called Shera – that means, it means . . . it's a wild beast. A tiger. I think it's a tiger.'

'Oh. Like Shere Khan?'

'Yes. And my grandad used to drive him to the nearest town.'

'Why did he go there?'

'To get corn – no, not corn, seed to grow corn, and he used to whip Shera to make him go faster, to get there before they sold it all, and my granny used to say, "Don't you dare to whip that horse." But my grandad never took any notice – he did when my granny rode with him in the seat, but when she wasn't there he used to whip Shera, because he never wanted to be late and he liked riding real fast. And one day, somebody saw him – a lady, and she told my granny, and when he got home, my granny said, "If you dare to whip that horse once more, I'll give you what-for." And when he took him to town again, do you know what he did? He waited, he waited till he got past the lady's village, and up over the other side of the hill, and he whipped him, to go real fast down the hill, and Shera went faster and faster, and then he stopped. My grandad went u-u-u-up into the trees and then down again, and landed on his bottom on the ground. And this little old man came up to him from behind a tree and said, "That just deserves you right."'

Most of Ahmed's stories end up with 'That just deserves you right' and a sagacious finger-wag.

'And in Pakistan there's devils, and they ride on your shoulder, and if you be naughty they pinch you, and – ew – it's horrible,' he says with an accompanying wince of remembrance. 'And there's hanging there. There is. Really. And this man in the next village, he was ever so very wicked, he made this other man dead all over 'cept for his eyeballs . . .'

'Dead all over . . . Don't tell lies.' I don't mind a few Polyfilla-lies, to stanch the gaps, as it were, and help the story along, but this seems a bit much.

'You can.' Ahmed nods his head wisely, back and forth.

'Oh no you can't.'

'Yes, you can,' he insists. 'They hang you for it. Only a few people know how to do it, and they hang them.'

'How can you make somebody dead all over except for their eyeballs?' I say indignantly.

'You can you *can*. They do that,' he explains carefully and slowly, so that I should appreciate the cunning of it, 'so the person who's dead can see he's dead.'

I'm temporarily thrown by this, and just sit.

'Across the road there's this lady, and she goes mad in the summer, she goes up and down Rosehill Street breaking windows and taking her clothes off. And then some men come and put her in a van, and she goes off with them and they put wires on her head. That's what Shabir said.' I look at him. 'In King's Field,' he says. 'Why do they put wires on their heads?'

'I don't know. They just do. It makes them forget things; they forget their problems for a while. They forget who they are and everything that's ever happened to them.'

'*Now* who's telling lies?' says Ahmed, jubilant and pointing.

'It's true. They used to come back afterwards blinking and staggering, one by one. Even though they had all been round the same breakfast table three hours before, they couldn't remember each other.'

'What I really like to hear about,' he says, 'is when you were in King's Field. I like to hear about all the hens and the pigs and the ducklings.'

'Yes, there were hens and lots of cows and some pigs and their piglets. And there was even a great big bull, goodness knows why. He was in a field by himself. And, er . . .'

'The mummy pig had five little piglets . . .' prompts Ahmed.

'Yes, the mummy pig had these five little piglets, and one afternoon when me and a friend . . .'

'Shirley.'

'Shirley. Me and Shirley, we went to see them, and the mother pig was fast asleep and snoring and her great round side was heaving u-u-u-up and down, u-u-u-up and down, like a huge inflatable balloon, and there were all the little piglets standing in a line on her side, going up and down too, having a ride.' Ahmed always looks charmed by this recollection, he clasps his hands in subdued glee.

'And what about what Nurse Petticoat said to Doris?'

'Pettigrew. Nurse Pettigrew. Well, there was this terrible stampede to the wash-room before breakfast, everybody pushing and shoving; it was like a herd of bison, and Nurse Petticoat – *Pettigrew* – she just pushes her way in and roars, "What's going on? I can see you Doris, you lot be quiet."'

'Oh no she didn't,' chimes in Ahmed definitely, '*she said . . .*'

He pauses while the words come to him exactly as he first heard my arbitrary recollection. 'She said, "Now then, what's going on in here? I can see you Doris – let's have a bit of hush."' He pokes bossily at the air.

'Yes. All right then, that's what she said.'

'Those wires – did you have them?'

'No. I was scared they'd make me. The day sister – she was terrible, she was a tartar – she said, "We've been told about you, you won't take your tablets, and you won't do as you're told. We're not having it, you'll get ready for treatment and if your name's down on my list you'll go, and that's that." And one of the nurses wouldn't let me have any breakfast, to be ready to go down, so I ran off and hid in the nurses' lavatories.'

Ahmed moves his folded hands delightedly. 'And didn't they find you?'

'No. And in the afternoon I went looking for the doctor, and when I found him I said, "I don't want those wires on my head. Do I have to have them?" And he said, "No." Then I said I'd been told to get ready for treatment that morning, and he said, "I give you my firm promise I will never authorise that treatment for you, and it doesn't matter what Sister this or Nurse that says. While I'm in charge here, my word stands."'

Doctor MacTangle – taken by a heart attack before he retired. Perhaps when you are responsible for all those people it wears you out in the heart, it's a terrible strain.

'Tell me about some more of the ladies – Little Red Riding Cook and Ellen-a-little-bit and all those.'

'Well, there was Night Sister, she was Irish, she was lovely. And Little Red Riding Cook. The nurses had these cloaks, navy with red inside, but they always wore them the navy way out. The cook's cloak was grey and red, but she wore it with all the red showing. She was very tiny and difficult – she had been a patient – and she had quite a few barnies with Day Sister. She rowed with everybody – patients, nurses, doctors. Everybody. And there was an Irish lady there, called Ellen, and she told us all about her baby, Ellen-Elizabeth. "Ellen-a-little-bit, her daddy calls her," she said, about her baby.

'Ellen had been an orphan, and she was happy now for the first time in her life. But, you see, she was having treatment, so she didn't remember her problems.' I pause, remembering Ellen and when they fetched her screaming from the trees, after the doctor had just told her her husband was leaving her.

June was thin as a streak of lightning, she wore a brilliantly red dress, her face was covered in old garnet-coloured scabs. I tried not to look as though I noticed them, but she said, 'I'm an epileptic, love, if you're looking at my scabs.'

'There was June, who wore red. And all around were lawns, and beyond that fields and fields . . .' I come to a halt again, and we stare into the flame that the British State will still be paying for next summer.

'And Lesley was pretty.'

'Yes, Lesley was pretty. I was a bit scared of her at first, she was quite a bit older than me, and tall, and she had a wild way of talking: she'd suddenly turn on somebody and tell them off and shriek at them. But while she was sleeping she was pretty.'

'I know – she had gold hair and lipstick.'

'No lipstick, but yes, she had gold hair. Corn-gold. And a dusty gold skin, and pink cheeks.'

'And every morning a lady used to watch Lesley wake up.'

'Yes.' I smile, remembering Ann heaving herself out of bed every morning to sit on the hard wood chair by Lesley's bed, waiting.

'I hadn't really thought of her as anything but thuggy, I suppose because I was a bit scared of her, and very wary. Anyway, Ann – she was expecting a baby and had two or three toddlers at home, so maybe she was missing them – I don't know – but she sat at Lesley's bedside every morning without fail. I was a lazy kid, but one morning I thought: What *is* this? and I got out of bed too, to see what was happening. Ann sat leaning over on her plump elbows on to the side of the narrow bed, and I sat on the bottom and watched both of them. Ann gave me a little smile, and went on watching, and I sat watching too. And Lesley, asleep, was really very pretty: her face was like a little girl's. So we sat and we watched her come back into the world, and when she opened her eyes we both smiled at her.'

'Why were the ladies in there – what had they done?'

'I can't really remember, it's a long time ago. Ann, I think, was suffering from exhaustion. Lesley – I don't know. Her mother had died when she was four and she'd had lots of foster-mothers as a child. I just don't know why she eventually landed up in King's Field.'

'I know what you mean. There's this girl at our school, her name's Stephanie Holmes, and she's got five mums. And when I first saw her she says, "Ugggh."' He lifts his voice in disdainful falsetto, '"Ugggh, don't come near me, I'm prejudiced." And I sit next to her on Thursdays in music, and that's the day when she goes to see her fifth mum, on Thursday tea times. She don't like her fifth mum, she's too little. Little mums aren't no good, are they?'

'Little m . . . young mums?'

He nods. 'And she never sees her first mum now; she ran away to Africa with a African. Her real father – she's never seen him – he's called Sherlock Holmes, and one day she plans on finding him.'

'Well, you'll have to be kind to her.'

'I am kind to her,' he says, sounding quite definite about this. 'Do you ever see any of those ladies who had the wires – what happened to them?'

'They all went home eventually. Yes, I sometimes see them around in shops and streets, but I can't remember their names. We don't speak, it's so long ago.'

'There's a lady and a man, she's got long grey hair, and she walks about pushing a pram. I looked inside that pram once, under the hood, and there's nothing there, only empty bottles. Did she come from King's Field?'

'I don't know. I can't remember.'

The winter evening has fallen, and I set out to walk with him to the main road. We walk rapidly through the evening and turn the corner, by the pub. The road across the top of the street goes abruptly narrow, seems as though it will run into the backs of gardens. A small street humps down into what appears to be no road at all, and then the road sprawls out, downwards and upwards and all askew. You can tell when people that are strangers come here; their cars come to a sudden jolting halt at the bottom of the small hilly street, and they peer out, blinking, wondering where on earth they are. Or cars that come horizontally often try to back out, the drivers thinking they can't get through, when all they have to do is to keep going. We walk by the unpavemented road outside the pub and turn into the slope of jaggedly widening road. Ahmed takes off, walking awry, neither in the middle nor the side, walking his own tipsy slope down the road.

'Come on to the pavement. Where do you think you're going?'

'No no *no*. This way,' he insists. 'I always walk this way at nights. Look!'

He turns to me and excitedly points ahead to the skyline, dark against the dark blue sky, between housetops the fluted dome of the Pentecostal church reflecting back rosy light from the unseen busy road below, with a slip of moon: it looks like a bit of Baghdad heaven.

'I told you.' He turns, very pleased with matters. 'Now, aren't you glad you came my way?' he wheedles. I nod and agree, cross my fingers we don't get knocked down, and muse for how much longer in a wide road his feet will unerringly walk the path that shows wonders.

Once home, I put the kettle on again, pull my nightdress on, and wrap myself round in a blanket. As I sit in front of the fire, I get to thinking of the ladies in King's Field, a long time ago.

June, of the violent red dress and scabbed face – I saw her last Christmas Eve in the supermarket, by the bread. She bends slightly and puts a loaf in her basket, whilst all about non-stop Elvis burbles across the acres of tins 'Blue blue blue Christmas'.

Her features haven't changed much in all these years; she has a strange birdlike air of detachment, her face knotted about with a headscarf, tidy and bright. Standing in the long queue to the check-out, I recall an afternoon tea-break at King's Fields. June and Cheryl and me, sitting over our coffee-cups for a long time, deciding not to go back for tea on the ward, but to stay in the deserted canteen and pay for our drinks, and talk. When June was fifteen she had stolen a pair of stockings. Being, she told us, hot-tempered and inclined to minor violence – which her epilepsy made appear worse – she had ended up in Rampton prison hospital. And there she was left to rot for ten years.

'I was a terrible kid. I know I was – I was awful, I didn't like anybody touching me and I used to throw things at people and scream at them. I was awful. There's no getting away from it. But I didn't deserve that.' She speaks distantly, as though every bit of anger has been bled away from her.

'Ten years of my life. It was Mr Noel-Baker got me out – I thought I'd never get out again. Every night in my prayers I say his name. I'd still be there now, if it wasn't for him.'

Cheryl comes back with the cups, newly-filled with more coffee. June reaches across the round plastic table-top, and my plump adolescent hand takes the imprint of her sharp nails.

'Oh, my love.' She speaks with a sudden passion I've never heard from any man. 'If I was to tell you the things that went off there, you'd never believe me.'

'Oh, my love' – lots of people say that to you, they aren't speaking to you but to themselves that they rescued.

'If I die and go to hell, it couldn't be worse than that place.' She talked on, but I can't remember what she said; perhaps my youth wanted to spare itself. All I remember is her nails stinging into my hand as she spoke.

I turn from the noisy queue and see her, moving across the tiled floor with her basket, looking like anybody else in her dun headscarf and brown coat.

Day Sister – she was awful. One afternoon, it was about six o'clock, just after the tea things had been cleared away, but about an hour before the visitors came. Day Sister came into the largest ward and said, 'I've heard enough of you people, you've been getting far too noisy all day, I'm locking the doors until you calm down,' and whipped straight out of the room and locked both the doors. There was nobody in bed, all the patients in this ward were up all day, and it was jam-packed full. There were about forty beds, in lines running from wall to wall, making a big deep square. And one after the other, like it was catching, a sort of wildness spread among the patients. I crept ever so quietly into the corner and sat on the corner bed, on the pillow, way out of the way. And this thing – it went from one to the other, along the lines of women, they went off like corks spitting out of bottles. Mrs Ormerod, she wasn't affected either; she went to the door and called softly, 'Sister? Sister Flanagan, do let me out,' and turned the knob a few times.

She thought *she* wasn't meant to be locked up. When one of the ladies went spinning off Mrs Ormerod got hit and scratched because she was in the way. Somebody threw themselves at the door, screaming, and somebody else threw themselves at the window and it broke. It was pandemonium. Flowers in their vases went over and there was water on the floor and on the beds. I pulled more and more into the corner, into the corner angle, so as not to get hit but mostly not to catch the wildness. A lady was crawling up the door, she wasn't wild either but she was frightened, she was crying. And in the middle of all this sat Nelly, looking contemptuous and sort of bored. She had been in hospital for a very long time, and had seen it all before, I suppose, lots of times. There she was, sitting like a rock with waves of hysteria breaking all around her.

For days afterwards everybody was walking around with bruises on them where they had smashed into beds and lockers. It was scary, seeing all those ladies – most of them had families and responsibilities – just seeing their expressions change when they let go of themselves. It happened so easily, so quickly. Later that night, just before bed time, they all sat talking together and drinking Horlicks and cocoa as though nothing had happened. That was really scary.

Then I was moved from the big general ward, up into the Circle. The Circle was this mad place; if you weren't disturbed before, you would be after you went there. It was a corridor, with small dormitories opening from it, and it curved round and came back to where it began. I'd been up there every day with a can to water the plants on the windowsills – the windows all looked on to this little round garden, but you couldn't get to it. The air was warm and heavy, and the plants were luxuriously thick but there were no flowers on them. I used to feel I wanted to trace my footsteps back the way I had come, for when I'd finished watering all the plants I'd arrived back where I'd started from. It was a weird feeling. Like you'd just been walking in nowhere.

Anyway, in the Circle the dormitories had only about six or eight beds in them. The patients sleeping there were mostly due to leave fairly soon, unless they were very long-stay, when they were allocated a private bedroom.

And when I was sleeping in the Circle, I went back to the

ward late one morning to get something from my locker, and I heard the doctor in the next room, which was the Treatment Room. It was the day for electric shocks. I heard the Doctor say something in a low normal voice, something like, 'Tell me, now Ethel . . .' and the woman started whimpering, and talking and crying to another person, who couldn't have been there. 'Oh, oh, oh no. Don't. Don't, Annie, no, don't do it – oh, oh, aaaaaah.' She screamed and cried like a little girl. I left the empty ward and ran down the curving corridor.

Lesley had been a patient for some months, and she slept in the Circle too. Then the doctor found her a job, and she started to go off to work in the mornings, and come back again to the hospital straight from work, for her tea. About the second or the third day she came back at midday, but she didn't come near the wards or any people, she strolled around the lawns with her shoulder-bag swinging, and we all watched her from inside. 'Lesley's back . . . Lesley's back.' She kept well away, but in sight. Finally, she must have got hungry, for she came in at tea time.

'And where have you been, madam? The doctor's going to have something to say to you,' said a nurse.

I was a bit scared of Lesley; she was very aggressive and although she laughed quite often, when she wasn't laughing she had a constant furrow in her brow.

After a time, Ann and the other patients in the Circle went home, leaving Lesley and me, and empty beds. I was glad I wasn't alone up there; it was spooky, I thought. No, nobody had died there. But it was warm and lighted and quiet, and well away from the main ward, and the silent Treatment Room was just next door, with the shades of all those people, screaming their souls out. Yet it was so quiet. I didn't even like leaving the ward to go to the lavatory. You could stand at the ward door and watch the corridor, running two ways in opposite directions yet leading to the same place. It made me feel dizzy.

'Just us two, we'll have some fun, darlin',' said Lesley. But there was nothing more exciting to do than iron our clothes, and talk.

On Lesley's locker-top was her writing-pad, which she had doodled all over: 'Lesley Wood, Lesley, Jimmy. Jimmy and

Lesley Wood. Jimmy and Lesley Wood. JIMMY. James Anthony Wood (with a scalloped box around it), Lesley and Jimmy. Jimmy. Jimmy.'

Jimmy was her brother, she said, but they had been split up when she was four or five, when her mother died, and Lesley had gone off to foster-parents. When she was about nine she stole something, something small from a shop, sweets or the like, and the court ordered her to be taken away from her foster-mother.

'You should have heard me scream, darlin', when they came. A policeman came and I was holding on to her and screaming . . .' She laughs. 'I didn't want to go. She was my favourite foster-mother. But I write to Jimmy. He's ten years older than me and he's married, and he says I can go to live with them as soon as I leave here, his wife says I can. She's nice, I really like her, she says she's looking forward to having me.' As if she had to prove this, she pushed around in her oblong box shoulder-bag and brought out a letter from Jimmy's wife to show me.

I stare into the flame, and remember one afternoon. It is very sunny, the Circle dormitory is full of brightness, the windows are open and the smell of fresh-mown grass is strong. In the distance comes the sound of the mower, still chuntering since the morning. I'm lying on my bed, reading. Patients aren't supposed to do this, but it's unlikely that any nurse will come way up here in the middle of the afternoon. I can't remember what it is I'm reading. Suddenly, the dormitory door flies open and in comes Lesley, smiling. She looks a little dazed. Her eyes shine.

'Hello, darlin'.' She sits then tentatively on a tiny piece of the bed next to mine. 'I've just had a shock. Something funny's just happened,' she says, half-laughing and gasping, as though with disbelief, behind her hand. 'I can't believe it.' Her eyes shine still. She disengages the strap of her bag from her shoulder and lets it fall away slowly on to the bed. 'The doctor's just told me I had a baby.' She looks at me, stunned, happy. 'I can't believe it.' Then a little ruck of slight disbelief appears between her brows. 'I can't believe it. It might be true. I don't know. I can't . . . I just can't believe it.'

She rubs her arms as though they are cold with unknowing, in spite of the sunshine pooling on to the light locker-tops and all about us on the white bedspreads.

'When he was telling me, I thought I did . . . I thought I could remember a little bit . . . Oh darlin', I still can't believe it.' She gives a small gasping laugh.

'Where's the baby?'

She looks at me, as though she never thought of that. 'I don't know. It was a little boy, I think. I think that's what he said. I don't know where he is.' After a moment she says, 'You know, I think it might be true . . .'

Well, it was a long time ago. She walks round the streets, pushing an old pram full of wine bottles, and she and her guy, they live at Mohammed's place now. They should be all right there. He will take them Lucozade when they are ill, little titbits on festival days.

I hold out my hands, more palpably to feel the fire, and feel all of us here together near its warmth – me and Ahmed – and Ahmed's granny who can't eat gingernuts and was taken to see the mummy, June, Lesley and her man, Stephanie Holmes who is going to look for her father. And Ann, who sat before Lesley's bed, so long ago, waiting for the miracle.

AT THE OLD ROSE

IT'S EARLY DECEMBER and I call in to see Sassy at The Old Rose Revived. I turn into the cobbled and dusty alley which leads to the back of the pub. Outside the back door stands an empty saucer, and a freshly-dug fir tree is propped against the wall.

'A real tree – lovely.'

'Yes, I like a real tree; the needles are a nuisance, but it's always a mess in here anyway, so it doesn't matter.'

That's what I like about Sassy; she is easy-going, she makes people feel at ease straightaway. Inside there is a spread of children's clothes and toys, teacups, ashtrays, knitting and sewing.

'Did you happen to see Mandy on your way in?'

'No, but her saucer is empty.' Mandy is their old cat.

'She's taken to staying away for a long time, since we had those terriers for a bit. She didn't like them.' Customers are always leaving things at The Old Rose; letters and postcards arrive from customers to other customers, messages are left, parcels. Just recently Sassy and Jack have been looking after two small dogs for one of their old regulars, Manchester Jim, who had to go into hospital.

'Manchester's out now, but he's not well, so we've found temporary homes for the dogs. We kept them for six weeks. It was driving us all up the wall, wasn't it, Paula?' Paula nods and smiles from the corner, bent over her sewing.

'Just a minute,' Sassy says suddenly under her breath, moving rapidly and silently across the room and seizing hold of the door-handle. Her actions remind me of ladies in cartoons, waiting behind doors with rolling-pins. She suddenly whips the door open sharply. A shadow moves up the stairs, but isn't quick enough.

'I can hear you, Peter.' The shadow makes a slight noise on the stairs, stops, and comes creaking down towards us. Peter fills the doorway – tall, thin, fair. He comes smiling in, nodding and pleasant. He would rather have been allowed to slip up the stairs, to bed and oblivion.

'I've got another letter here about you,' starts Sassy. 'Honestly, Carol, you've no idea what a trouble he is; if it's not one thing it's another. I've got to go to court with him next week.'

Peter sits easily in the armchair, as though his mother is speaking about an acquaintance and nothing to do with him. He and his friends broke into the local supermarket one evening, and were found strolling around between the aisles of food, indifferent to the groceries and to the alarm systems that were belting away at full blast all around them.

'And he won't go to school, whatever I do. That's what the letter's about.'

'What's the point of going? I don't like it; we don't learn anything,' he says in a reasonable tone of voice.

'Well, what do you do when you're not at school?'

'I enjoy myself. I do as I like.'

'Don't ask him what he does. I don't know what he does all day, and I'm sick of it. Whatever you do or say to him, he won't go; he doesn't take any notice . . .' says Sassy. Peter smiles as though humouring us all, and Paula lifts her head briefly, and smiles.

'But you need to be educated. You won't know much if you don't go to school.'

'Oh yes I will. In any case – what's the point? I don't like the lessons, I don't like most of the teachers, most of them don't like me, and none of us will get jobs anyway.' He smiles and lifts his hands reasonably, as though it is out of his control, as though he has faced reality and is determined to be casual and cheerful about it.

'There's no point.' None of us contradict him. Then again, as we stay silent, 'It doesn't matter.'

'But it does matter, it is worth learning things, even though it doesn't seem to be. Once you know something, nobody can take it from you. The Greeks thought that if a candle once shines, even if it's blown out straightaway, it changes everything; the whole world can never be as though that light had never shone.' I heard this somewhere and it turns me on, so when I get excited it comes spewing out. Peter's mouth falls half-agape; silent, he blinks, splintering blue light into the room.

'Yes, that's right, I agree with that,' says Sassy, getting excited too. 'You need to be at school, you don't know what you want at your age, and I'm absolutely sick to death of getting letters about you and having social workers round . . .'

'All right, keep your hat on.' He hasn't lost his temper once, he rarely does. Perhaps he thinks it is what other people do.

'When I was your age we had to go to school, and that was that. There was no maybe.'

'In my grandfather's time they swooped one morning and rounded up all the parents who hadn't sent their children to school, and took them to the gaol. My father could remember it happening.'

Peter rocks with laughter and thumps the settee arm delightedly. 'That's it. That's right. That's what they ought to do – they'll be coming for you, Ma, with their big van.'

'Don't talk stupid, Peter,' shrills Sassy indignantly. 'Why should they come for me when it's you that won't go to school?' She changes tack suddenly. 'Anyway, I'm sick of all this school business. The school never taught him to read. It was me that taught him. He was well gone nine, Carol, and he couldn't read a word. I knew I had to do something. I dropped everything and kept him off school for a week so's I could teach him to read. And now he won't go. He's been difficult ever since.'

Peter looks up, smiling. 'And you can just take that smile off your face.'

He smiles some more, shaking his head, conceding graciously, 'It's true. My mum taught me to read.' He sits awhile opening and closing his hands, and then nods good night, affable and pleasant.

Sassy leans back in her chair and blows out her cheeks. 'Phew! Honestly! I've had more trouble with him than the rest of them put together.'

Paula twitches her needle into her work and puts it aside. 'I'll make a cup of tea.' And off she goes.

Sassy leans forward and lowers her voice, searching my face as she speaks. 'Glue. And lighter fuel.'

'Are you sure? He doesn't look – he doesn't look ill, or anything.'

'I've found the cans under his bed, Carol.'

I don't know what to say. What can you say?

When Sassy's last baby was born, three years ago, she lost her mind. For six months the wind blew about inside her head, it was open to the elements, and her children were all dispersed to the homes of strangers until she was better.

'Oh, that's lovely, Paula. Thank you,' says Sassy, taking the cup. Paula is tiny and dark – when she isn't fair – and although at seventeen she is three years older than Peter, she is little more than half his height.

'Look at her sewing.' She ruffles at a piece of blue cotton that Paula is making into a blouse. 'She won't finish it,' says Sassy in a low voice. 'But I don't say anything, because she might. I worry about her. She was sent to several families when I was in hospital, so she was upset quite a lot. Then she moved in with a very nice couple; they all got on and she liked it there. She used to visit them regularly, even after she came back home. But they've split up now. That upset her quite a bit. Anyway, she doesn't seem too bad now, so I'm keeping my fingers crossed . . .'

Paula has never had a job since leaving school, she can't get one. And after that, she can't want to get one. She is now at the stage where anything she wants to do or to have, no matter how apparently easy, is impossible. She is starting to learn, step by step, how to fail.

'I put my name down for a little cat,' says Paula, coming back with her tea.

'You have to put your name down for a *cat*? A pedigree cat?'

'No, any cat. I don't mind,' she says, vague and smiling.

'I don't think it's fair on Mandy to have a kitten. She's getting on now.'

'No, I mean for me, when I leave. To take with me.'

'Oh yes, when you leave,' says Sassy, smiling. Paula has her name down on a housing list, and every so often packs her suitcase, and there it stands in her bedroom, until she unpacks it again.

'Look at those awful curtains. I'll have to wash them before Christmas. And the settee-cover. Look at it. Not that it's worth bothering with the settee much. It's old now, the children have jumped all over it – look where our PJ has cut a bit out of it, the little devil . . . And Mandy keeps sharpening her claws on the arms. Somebody is going to have to sleep on it at Christmas, when Nan comes. I don't know who. She had Peter's bed last year. He was in the children's home then. She's too old to sleep on it, if she fell off . . . and it's not very comfortable for her . . .' She ponders on a while. 'The children will have to stay in their beds, and I can't have Peter on the settee; he still wets, Carol, at nights. I've got a feeling it's going to end up being me,' she finishes, with glum logic.

'I'll sleep on it, Mum, I don't mind.'

'No, you won't. She's still in her frilly nightie at midday.' Paula giggles. 'And I'm not stepping round you; it gets on my nerves when I'm trying to get the dinner and you're lying round in your frills, smoking.'

We laugh. 'No. She's very good really, she does help out, but it's always afterwards, with the washing-up.'

'What are you talking about? I made the stuffing last year, and I set the table.'

'Yes, you did,' laughs Sassy. Then she changes tone suddenly. 'It might just as well be Jack, really, on the settee. He'll stay up most of the night anyway, in the pub, with being closed the next day. But if I suggest it to him, he'll create.'

Paula abandons her sewing and curls further into her chair, hauling the cat, who has just crawled from behind the settee, on to her lap. 'Are you going to the midnight mass?'

'Might do. I didn't go last year.'

'Is that at St James's? I've seen photos of you and Mum there, in bridesmaid's dresses when Aunty Joan and Uncle Ted got married.'

Sassy pokes a spill into the fire, lights her cigarette, and starts on a story, to cheer us up. 'You know, years ago, when I'd just started nursing, there was this old lady – Granny Thornley, she was called. Well, it's some years ago and she was ninety-three then, so . . .'

Her voice fades away; we watch the firelight glowing on the drying clothes, and sip our tea in unison. She takes up her tale again.

'Well. In the afternoons if we weren't busy we'd try to spend a bit of time with the old ones, and talk to them. And one afternoon I was sitting with Granny Thornley. She never had any visitors, and when you spoke to her you had to hold her hand and speak slowly, and bend right near her face to catch what she said. And I said to her, "Tell me, Granny, where were you married?"

'And she leaned forward – she was ever so frail – ever so frail – and she said, "St James's. When I was seventeen." And she clutched my hand tightly.

'"*Did* you? I went there when I was a little girl. And what did you wear?"'

Granny's voice floats out, a wisp of air that will soon be gone, '"Cream silk. And peonies. And I went to church in a carriage."'

Some might think it a liberty, calling old patients granny, a negation of their personality, but if you were very old and didn't get any visitors and a young nurse sat on your bed and called you granny and gave you a cuddle, well – I guess you wouldn't much mind.

'Yes – "I went to church in a carriage,"' Sassy repeats triumphantly, and she leans back from her story, back into her life, smiling and cheered.

We leave; Sassy and Paula walk back with me to my doorstep, as it's late.

'Merry Christmas,' I call, and their voices bell away into the dark streets, one under the other, 'Merry Christmas . . .'

'Merry Christmas . . .'

'Merry Christmas . . .'

After Christmas I hear how the settee problem resolved itself. Sassy and her children slept in their beds, and their nan slept at home and came in the morning in a taxi. But the settee wasn't empty.

On Christmas Eve in the sitting-room at the back of The Old Rose, Paula is filling stockings and her mother is arranging mince pies on doilied plates. The small children have gone willingly to bed and so has Peter. Sassy's husband Jack is busy in the pub; it is in full swing now. He comes through to get a bucket and mop from the kitchen. It is getting late, nearly twelve, but the regulars are clinging to the bar-stools. Paula is just putting a sugar mouse into PJ's stocking, when Jack shoves open the door again. This time he is carrying not mop and bucket but a little girl, about seven years old. She is drowsy, and doesn't resist as Jack lowers her on to the settee.

'She's been left in the Club Room. Her mother's got custody of her over Christmas but she's gone off. She's going to collect her tomorrow.'

'What – Christmas Day?'

Jack shrugs, and moves back into his own territory.

'What's your name?' asks Paula kindly, but the child says nothing.

'I expect she's tired. Are you tired, or would you like a drink, my love? Paula will get you a milk drink in a minute,' says Sassy. Paula finds her an old teddy, and starts to read her a story, but the child still doesn't speak. Sassy bustles back with a blanket, and tucks it round her.

On the settee under the Christmas tree sits the little girl. She doesn't move, stays put; it's like she has no legs, she just stays exactly where she has been put, under the blanket. Before they leave, switching out the lights but leaving on the tree lights, Sassy reaches up and pulls off a gingerbread heart from the tree and gives it to the child to eat. When they have gone the child sits watching the lights. In a little while the gingerbread rolls from her fingers.

At four o'clock on Christmas morning the last of the regulars creep down the pub yard, singing under their breaths and stumbling. Jack leaves the empty glasses on the tables, switches the light, and goes to bed. The child on the settee is unsleeping: she stares into the shadows of the unfamiliar room and in her hand she clutches a star that has fallen from the tree.

Later in the morning the child still sits heaped up on the settee, obediently trailing a spoon after puffed wheat in a basin, and still clutching the star. A hastily wrapped parcel which Sassy has just given to her is still unopened on the settee arm.

'What's Santa bringing you for Christmas? Do you know? I bet it's something nice.'

The child looks back at her as though she would like to understand what she is saying, but can't. About a full minute later she opens her lips with a little gasp and says quietly, 'A doll.' Then she looks at the floor.

'A dolly. How lovely,' says Sassy, enthusing over it as though it were there, whilst rolling on an extra jumper and pulling it down, and wondering whether to peel more potatoes, in case the child's mother doesn't collect her.

Paula comes downstairs, wearing new beads over her dressing-gown. She has just barracked the small children in their bedroom with their presents, so as not to upset the little girl. She bends down to the settee to speak to the child.

'Merry Christm . . . Why, whatever have you done?' says Paula, peering more closely.

Over the blanket and the settee and all up the child's wrist and lower arm is plastered wet and dried blood, her fingers scarlet and fixed round the star, transparent and silvered, clutched so tightly it has smashed into her hand.

'Let me see, my lovey, let Aunty Sassy see your hand . . .' Sassy bustles in from the kitchen. Unresisting, the child lets its fingers be prised open one by one.

'Oh Mum, look. Had I better get the tweezers?' Fragments of silvered glass have embedded in the small palm, like bits of shrapnel. The hand is bathed, kissed, shards are recovered from it, disinfectant waved about, Elastoplast . . . In the distance voices waver, '. . . can't understand how she didn't feel anything,' as the two strange kind females hover above like big birds. The child closes her eyes, into her own night, where a dazzling light burns and blisters deep inside her.

WINTER

THE TOWN'S STREETS in early December are black and alive with rain. I wander down an empty precinct, nearer and nearer a man in jeans, playing a guitar. 'How many roads must a man wa-a-alk down . . .' He looks as though he comes from the past. I haven't heard the song or the simple style of singing for years, and am greatly moved, want to cry. There don't seem to be any of those people around any more. He belongs to the past, and so do I.

'". . . the answer, my friend, is blowin' in the – " thank you, dear – "wind, the answer is blowin' in the wind . . ."' I've delved into my purse but feel I want to drop more than a coin into his near-empty guitar case. Will a tear do? I hate Christmas.

On the way to the bus-stop see Cherry, who used to live where I live now. She and her little girl are running in the rainy dark, holding hands and laughing and jumping the puddles, their dreadlocks flying. It looks a lot of fun. She sees me and I see her and we recognise each other. Mail came for her for some time after she left, and I'm still using the half of a Babygro she left in the bathroom as a cleaning cloth. And here is the baby, jumping puddles.

Assemble the presents for wrapping – hand-embroidered Chinese slippers from the local chemists for £1.35; from the market, pink and blue pearls for sisters; a box of bricks; books; a doll; a rubber dinosaur smelling of strawberries; knitted mittens. Boxes of plums in chocolate from the Polish shop. Somebody is going to get a nice half-used roll of Sellotape in with their present, I think. I can't find it. Mixed up with the hollied paper and festive stickers are last year's stickers with a bit of green ink holly and the bright words 'Coël not Doël'. A whole year ago.

My aunty makes a cake, and I get in a bottle of sherry and boxes of mince pies, in case anybody comes round. But otherwise, I can't be bothered, just get the usual things. About three years ago now I prayed the best prayer I ever prayed, but all it was was 'Ooo God, Ooo . . . Ooo . . . Thank you. Thank you. Ooo . . .' because there was this tune going round and round in my head and I was so thrilled to be inside it. I rarely pray, as the adult part of me is often an atheist, but that's the part that clocks off fairly frequently, and the child bit is left to manage as best it can. It's a bit like the sympathetic and parasympathetic systems in the body, I *think*. Anyway, every December now I try to make up six carol tunes, so by the time I peg out there should be quite a few. But only manage two this year, before flu sets in.

On Christmas Eve Ahmed comes round and does the last minute shopping, as I'm snuffling and streaming away.

'Our house is full of cousins,' he says disgustedly.

'Now listen, I only want the things on the list. I don't want bubbly-gum, banana mousses that are good value . . .' I will have to say this several times, because on the few occasions he has shopped for me Ahmed always tried to improve on the shopping list.

'I think you need fish fingers,' he says.

'No, I don't – oh, all right.' I cave in ungraciously. He'll probably get them anyway.

'And what about some of those biscuits that aren't nice biscuits,' he says gleefully. He means Nice biscuits.

'Now, you aren't to go in the arboretum, looking for that woman.'

'Well, you're too late, because I've already been there and I never saw her.'

'You little . . . I knew you'd go looking for her – you should keep out of there on Christmas Eve. If you want to get mugged, do it when you're carrying your money about, not my money.'

I rattle on at him, but he probably won't take much notice, because he has been fascinated for a year now, and greatly amused by what happened to me in the park last Christmas Eve when I was stopped by a woman beggar. I handed her 20p to get a cup of tea, and she kept saying, 'No – £10, £10,' and trying to give it me back. After that, she followed me for a bit shouting roughly, '£10 . . . £10 . . . £10 . . .' and trying to knock at me with her shoulder, until I turned round and shouted back at her, 'Is your name Gladys?' because she reminded me of a friend of my mother's – not that *she'd* be begging in the park on Christmas Eve – in fact, she's dead. And when I shouted this at her, she stopped and stood there. It was just coming dusk. It was a strange thing.

The beginning of another year. I gaze out of the window at old snow and bright sunshine, through a fluey haze, and stay inside, swaddled in blankets, sucking orange segments and feeling like the Loathly Lady. January and February must be the rottenest months of the year; the Romans showed good sense in not having them. Inside here nightdresses and underwear lie drying on top of the fire, reindeer march around my cocoa mug, and the busy Lizzie Gail gave me is blooming away on the windowsill. I haven't seen Gail for well over two months, although she only lives next door but one. It's so cold, nobody goes out, unless they must.

Ahmed comes round, and sits plundering the new calendar on the mantelpiece, whipping up the pages and reading out the mottoes and maxims.

'"Men do not realise how great a revenue thrift is" – what about that, Carol?'

'I've got a headache.'

But he has flapped over the next sheet. '"Success is often failure with a new coat of paint,"' he reads musingly and then, seeing my look, 'Just one more – "A girl likes to be thought a picture but she hates to be called a sketch,"' he stumbles.

This eruption of Victorian demotic floors him completely, as it might any child. He sits scowling at it. I think of it being copied out laboriously and mindlessly from calendar to calendar, year in year out, for about a hundred years. Oh my God.

'Ahmed, if you don't stop that I think I shall *scream*.'

'No, just one more . . .'

Stagger and cough my way downstairs. It's freezing. I put on the kettle for tea and wash my hands in the lukewarm water from the water bottle. The tap water is icy. Bump into Paula at the labour exchange; she's huddled against the wall in a fur wrap, looking very turned off, awaiting the supervisor's pleasure. She has to sign on every day now, as a penance for being late. The result of this is that she doesn't dare go to bed at nights, for fear of not getting up.

'I sat up until six o'clock this morning and then fell asleep in the chair. If Mum hadn't woken me I'd have still been late, after all that.'

She seems in a lethargic kind of panic. '*And* it's rained on my new hairstyle.' She looks up ruefully from under sodden titian snails, and grins. When the supervisor finally shows up he doesn't look at her once, throws the signing sheet at her whilst looking in completely the opposite direction, like Perseus averting his face. Then he strolls back.

'I don't mind him,' she says. 'He hardly ever says anything. Like you're not there. It's the ones that come out and go for you I don't like.'

Mrs Holmes is supposed to be coming in for a New Year's drink, so I make biscuits. They turn out a bit wrong: the moons have turned into little fat cakes, the stars are curling up all their toes, and the hearts look decidedly scleroid, but I ice them anyway, pink and white. The recipe is from a wartime cookery book, and I feel quite luxurious using shell eggs, as the recipe says use them if you can get them. It's like when I'm eating hot buttered toast, I always think of George Orwell in the Catalonian trenches, and it makes me feel lucky. Mrs Holmes doesn't want to leave her fire; it's too cold. So I go to hers, and we sit sipping sherry and nibbling at Christmas cake, and the biscuits.

With an almighty effort, I go on a round of post office to cash my Giro, chemist for tonic, ironmonger's for paraffin, and supermarket, filling the trolley and crashing it home through the snow-filled streets.

A thaw has set in, and it rains. It's so miserable, it's like all around us life is drip-dripping away. In the evenings I go upstairs early and put the lights out, and the cats cluster round the fire and heap up around me on the bed, and I feel like primitive man in the darkness with his fire and his beasts. I lie listening to Mozart through the noise of the drips in the bathroom; every bucket and bowl is gathered underneath the bathroom ceiling, and it sounds as though there is a microphone in there too, magnifying the sounds of the water, echoing all about upstairs.

Stand at the doorway nattering to small Dean from the bottom of the street, when who should walk past but Gail. We hail each other like long-lost sisters and she comes in for a drink.

'It's been really hectic at the pub – I just haven't had a minute. I'm full-time now. I didn't want to be, but I couldn't manage on part-time money. They didn't make it up at Social Security, and I was still having to sign on every week and not getting anything. But when I've finished I'm absolutely exhausted, I really am. And do you know what, now? I could weep, Carol, I could – they've sent me a letter saying I've got to pay them £800 for being on Social Security. It's something they've just come up with. £800. They're stopping me every week now, and I don't earn much, as it is. The government doesn't want people to get jobs, I don't care what they *say* – On yer bike and all that – it's just cobblers; they don't want people to go to work, they want them to stop at home and draw their bit of money and not cause any trouble. That's what they want, and nobody's going to tell me different, because I shan't believe them. £800. I've never had £800 in my life. They're making things as difficult as possible for the people who *want* to work. That's what gets me . . .'

She asks me round the following week, on her night off, to meet her new fancy-pants. She looks very pretty in a pink fluffy sweater, and has made real coffee. We sit in her front sitting-room, surrounded by plants and pottery cats, and her big Baby on the rug. Her new bloke is fair-haired and moderately amiable, and sits politely as we chat on, getting through the accumulated gossip of two months. She says there's an *itch* going round. When we get to the inevitable bitching about the Social Security, the council, the government . . .

'Oh,' Mike breaks in, as though he's just remembered. 'Thatcher's coming to our place tomorrow.'

'What do you mean?'

'She's coming. There's a right to-do – the place'll be full of security guards, there's going to be snipers on all the roofs. We've all been told to bring our identity cards, with the photographs, or we'll be turned away. Doesn't matter how long you've worked there; if you haven't got your pass tomorrow, you can't go to work. Well, they've had it from me, because I've lost mine,' he finishes triumphantly, folding his arms high across his front.

'No you haven't.'

'I have, I tell you. There won't be anybody seeing my pass tomorrow. I don't care if they do send me home. Best place. I shall be back here by six in the morning – straight to bed.'

'Oh no you won't,' sparks Gail furiously, and turns and grins at me. 'Anyway, I don't know how she's got the nerve to push her chops in round here, after what her lot were going to do to Royce's, a bit back.'

'You're not kidding. I don't like any of them, but I always vote.'

'We-e-e-e-ell,' starts Mike easily, 'what's the point of it, they're all the same. I don't bother myself with it,' he says, easy and comfortable in his chair.

I could just pinch him. She looks as though she's going to as well, as soon as I've gone.

'I've *always* voted. I've never not voted, in spite of the rubbish you get landed with afterwards. It's people like you,' she looks over at him as though he's some reprehensible thing that belongs on the floor but has dared to crawl up and sit in the chair, 'that have got this country into the state it's in. This country used to be great. People who don't vote – they make me sick. You make me sick. You deserve all you get . . .'

'Have you ever been in The Mafeking? You must come, it's nice. I'm on duty on . . .'

The next morning I wake early; behind the thin flowered curtains is a brilliant white glow. It must have snowed again. Sleepily I wonder whether they let Mike in, or whether he biked home in the snow and was back snuggling in bed with Gail before half-past six.

On the wireless that day comes the news of the US Challenger tragedy, those poor people killed in their capsule. 'But the spirit of freedom will continue,' says the British Prime Minister, who was elected by less than one third of the electorate and speaks surrounded by security police and snipers.

Snow Snow SNOW.

Walking in the streets on a bright stardusty evening. All around, the darkness is prickling with noises, and coming towards me a man and a girl. He is carrying a box to his ear, holding it with his hands delicately about it, as though it's a precious treasure, which it is: the reggae coming from it is keeping him going.

February 8th – a sunny morning; sparse snowflakes like feathers float gently in the air. Sassy calls round.

'I've not moved from my fire unless I've had to – been suffering from idle-itis. Always get it at this time of year. I was on my way to see Beryl at The Minstrel Boy, so thought I'd call round and see how you are.'

Sassy seems to call on most of the other pub landladies round here. Apart from Beryl at The Minstrel Boy, there's Narinder at The Crown, Ethel at The Mafeking, and Maureen at The Bricklayer's Arms. And that Val at The Merry Wives, whom Sassy does *not* call on.

'Aren't you calling to see Pearl at The Crystal Palace?' I ask.

Sassy laughs. She always laughs now when I ask her that, because I like to hear her say it. It sounds as though she's on calling terms with the Snow Queen. She says there's an *itch* going round.

'I've heard.' Of course, I don't specially want the *itch* but in a way I don't mind because it links you up to everybody else, everybody that's got it, and I don't see many people in winter.

In the street Roxana and her brothers and Emmaline and her brothers are snowballing one another. It's the boys against the girls. The girls stay near their cache of ammunition, piled up on a car bonnet. The boys hurl themselves about the street with wild cries, swooping and yelling. Emmaline looks fetching in her pink Christmas ear-muffs; Roxana, with newly-shorn hair and her pyjamas tucked into stout boots, she looks like a small girl of the Steppes.

February 14th – Gail and Mike's wedding day. They take off to the registry office through a veil of snowflakes.

A report on the news says cruelty to children and baby-battering cases are way up from last year. Then the RSPCA's annual report comes out and says cruelty cases involving animals are up by a third from last year. Whatever is happening in the country?

It's March, it's spring, and wartime.

This time last year Mrs Holmes threw two buckets of water over the wall, in front of my window. Ostensibly this was a protest at my suffering the presence of a noisy stray tom in my garden. But the gesture was probably territorial. It was a whole year ago. She probably won't throw any buckets of water this year. As for the tom-cat, a small but spunky tabby, he is here again this spring, fighting all the other toms; there are cat-fights going on throughout the nights.

The street is starting to fill with children, now the better weather is here. On the corner at the top of the hill the pub is big and brick-red, with a wide arched doorway, studded with ornamental brick flowers. There are two pub signs, one showing a jolly old man, orange-clad, with a hearty red face. He is plainly the Falstaff of the pub's name. Round the corner in our street, the brewery have hung another sign – a gloomy-faced dark-haired man, wearing a big black hat. One hand is placed on his wide black belt, which in a casual glance gives the impression of being a big Bible; in the other hand is a most improbable glass of beer. He looks distinctly unhappy, as though he rather suspects someone is trying to make a fool of him.

On the street there is skipping and ball games, and round the corner in an empty garden Polly and Zahia have built a den. A clump of children come to show six-year-old Chris's nose, bloody where a teenage boy threw a brick at him.

Ahmed comes, full of the latest news.

'Guess what – the Canes are back and they have a new gang now, the New Gang. The Old Gang – they were the awfullest. They used to organise bike-thievery, and take it in turns to take our mosque money off of us. They're back now.'

Small Dean comes, with newspapers for the cats, and a collection of small boys.

'How's Chris, is he better now?'

'Yes, thank you. He went to school the day afterwards,' says his sister.

'What, with this nose?'

'Yes,' puts in nine-year-old Andy, 'he went with his nose because his nose didn't fall off,' and he bubbles up into home-made glee. He nudges Dean happily. 'I said, he went with his nose because . . .'

Call round at The Old Rose. Sassy is worried about Paula.

'I don't know what to do with her; I've had enough of her and Jack's fed up with her as well. She's in and out, coming and going like a yo-yo. She stopped going to her tech. course before the first term was over. She won't give a hand in the pub – won't lift a finger. She did use to help out on a Wednesday evening, but she's stopped that now. She's been through all my nail varnishes that I try to keep together, for when I do the old people's nails at the hospital. It might sound daft, but it brightens them up to have their nails done. The little madam's picked out the best colours and helped herself to them. I don't understand it – she was never any trouble when she was a little girl. At the weekend her and Maria and Bronia came back – they'd been thrown out of Paradise, because Bronia spat at a bouncer. She can't stand bouncers. Hates them. Anyway, they were all absolutely . . . well, she couldn't stand up.'

'Crikey, Sassy, we used to drink at that age.'

'I know that. Sometimes I was drinking on the Saturday, and then on the Sunday as well, when I first started drinking. But I still had to get up and do a day's work on the Monday. But she doesn't have to do that, she just lies around all the time. I don't see any end to it. I don't.

'It came to a head last weekend. Jack ticked her off about some of the friends she's been bringing in up the back stairs, and she flounced out. She went straight upstairs and packed her case, and she's gone off with it this time. I did forbid her to go in the middle of the night – I sat on the case. So she waited until she saw daybreak, and she was off.'

Gail must have locked Mike out last night: he was walloping the knocker on her door, the noise echoing about the street in the middle of the night.

'You know the word nigger, is it swearing?' asks Ahmed. 'I always thought it was swearing.'

When he was smaller he used to get the words nigger and bugger mixed up. This confused me for ages, until one day the council, in a great display of corporate pride, sent a painter round to paint all their houses in the street colour. He had a white YOPS boy with him.

'What have you done wrong now, you daft bugger,' said the painter.

'I thought it was very funny,' recalled small Ahmed, 'when the painter called that boy a daft nigger.'

'It's not swearing but people don't like it. Toughen up. I'm a bastard but I don't blow a gasket when people chuck the word bastard about.'

'I'm not a bastard,' says Ahmed with great satisfaction.

'You're not supposed to say Red Indian either. My real father was American and, you know, I'm wondering if he wasn't a Red Indian, a little bit.'

'You said last week your father was Irish.'

'Different week. Different dad.' I study myself in the mirror. 'I think I might be a Red Indian. I think I look like a Red Indian. What do you think?'

'A bit,' he says. Then, with considerably more interest, 'I think I might be, too.'

He seizes the hairbrush and starts rearranging his hair. From a chest I pull out a photograph of Rain-in-the-face, one of the last and handsomest of the Sioux warriors, and prop it against the mantelpiece.

'He was killed in battle, just after that was taken. Isn't he smashing?'

Ahmed is winding a belt round his head. 'Where's your real Red Indian eagle feather that was given to you by a real Red Indian?'

A further scrabble in the chest, and out comes the feather. He sticks it into the belt on his head, and makes marks with an eyeshadow stick down his face, to look like Rain-in-the-face's tattoo tears.

He turns to me triumphantly. 'See? I'm a real Red Indian now.'

The Jehovah Witness girls are back again, preparing for Easter. People come out of their houses on to the street, tinkering with their cars, washing their front windows and hanging fresh nets. I stand a jug of daffodils in the front window.

On Palm Sunday morning the Salvation Army plays at the top of the street, trumpets flashing back sunlight. People stand at their doors listening, as two bonneted ladies come round with buckets, for the donations. Usually it's Pam from down the street who comes, but she's not too well. She's been suffering with a bad back, and last autumn she and Trisha went off to a faith healer who had come all the way from Nigeria. Perhaps she'll come collecting next time, when her back is better.

'Carol do you like the Pope I don't like the Pope the Pope makes people eat fish and chips,' begins Ahmed, straight out of the blue and without pause.

'What's wrong with fish and chips?'

He makes indignant eyes. 'You shouldn't *make* people . . .'

'Er, you know, I don't think he does.'

Ahmed thinks Jehovah's Witnesses are the most intelligent people he has ever met.

'It's at Kingdom Hall; it's not like the Church of England and the Pope, everybody gets a go. They've got a platform there, and anybody can go on it. This lady came round, her name was Winnie, and she was a nice lady, she said I could call her Aunty Winnie, and if I saved up I could have this book. So I gave her 10p every week till I'd saved £1.50, and she said it was really £2 but she let me have it.'

I stare, horrified but impressed. He doesn't get much money.

'You mean you gave this woman £1.50 just for one of their blinking books?'

'It was a proper thick book, a big red one. It . . .' He casts about and suddenly seines in from adult conversation, 'it was well worth it.'

'What was so very marvellous about it?'

'It was full of stories. Oh Carol, lovely stories about good people, how the bones of their bodies were left on earth and all their flesh flowed into the shining perfect light . . . I'll bring it if you want to read it,' he says enthusiastically.

'No thank you, I'd rather you tell me.'

'Well, I'm not going to. You can read it yourself,' he replies, suddenly sullen.

The girl at the doorstep is dark-eyed and has a warm breathy voice as she assures me of God's care.

'We've no way of really understanding how much He loves us, how nice He's going to make it for us, if only we keep His Commandments. We've no idea what it's going to be like; we can't possibly know how beautiful it's going to be . . .'

'Well,' chips in the other girl who is big and fair and rather more tetchy. 'It isn't all . . . you know. I mean, He isn't soft. He has Standards,' she says fiercely.

'Ooooo yes.'

'No, but what I mean is, it isn't all easy. We've got to struggle to do His wishes. He'll be coming to judge us, you know, He'll send a Second Ark for His chosen, and everybody else – they'll be sorry, but it'll be too late. It's hard work sometimes, keeping His Commandments, but it will be worth it. All this nuclear power and stuff,' she says vaguely. 'I mean, that's wrong. That's man's wickedness for you. That isn't God. And all these streets – they could be so beautiful; people shouldn't have to live in streets like this. In God's world, as He meant it for us – there wouldn't be streets like this. There'd be no nuclear bombs, no starvation, no wickedness . . . Me, I'm very fond of poetry, but just think how much better all the poetry in the world would be, if everybody loved God and kept His Commandments . . . We haven't even begun to live yet . . .'

'You don't think perhaps poetry is born out of pain?'

'Pain? No. Pain isn't God's intention for His world. It's our sin that causes pain . . . Only a perverted person would like pain. Nobody likes pain.'

'I like pain. Well, no, I don't much, but I like to cry. It's my party and I'll cry if I want to.'

They giggle. Then the dark-eyed girl says coaxingly, 'But think how lovely He's going to make it for us, in His Kingdom, full of everybody keeping His will. They'll have free choice, of course, but they'll choose to be happy, to keep His will. If they don't, well, they'll soon be on their way out again . . .' She comes to a grinding halt.

I laugh out loud. Then so does she. We all three shake with laughter at Vanessa's enthusiasm carrying her away and causing her to etch in slightly more of the picture than she intended.

THE DAY OF JUDGEMENT

THE SUN STREAMS through the thin bedroom curtains, waking me earlier than usual. Outside, the street lies quiet, streaming with sunshine, and the rolling sound of the milk van's wheels can be heard. I hurry on my slippers and dressing-gown, even though it is early, for I feel restive. One of the Shaws moves coat-hangers against the wall, so they must be up too.

As I fill the kettle I sing. It is Saturday morning, it is spring, and I feel cheerful. I rip back the curtains and shove a way clear on the table for my plate of toast. The table is piled high with books, notebooks, tablets, hairgrips, cups, clothes and paper hankies. As I clear the way two hairgrips drop and a piece of paper flutters to the floor. With my toast-free hand I push it back on to the heap on the table. 'The Lord will send . . .' it starts. It was left in the week by the Jehovah's Witness girls, Paula and Vanessa.

Just as I'm watering the plants on the windowsill the line prop comes over from next door and taps on the window. It's Mrs Holmes knocking. I scurry out, as she might want some shopping fetched back.

'I thought I'd better let you know. They're saying there's going to be a Flood today, and an Ark will be calling at the top of the street. It's the Day of Judgement, they say.'

I ponder slowly on this information. 'Who says?'

'Well, when I went to fetch my milk in, the milkman told

me that the Ark's coming this morning. I'm no wiser than that, really.'

I nod thanks, and come back inside. It's really a bit of a nuisance, I'd wanted to go shopping.

Mrs Holmes prudentially takes in her washing, just in case, slips on her coat, and goes off to try to get a seat. Gail is grimly hanging out her washing, as though to defy the idea of the Ark, her face screwed up against the heavens in the perfect image of a gargoyle. She doesn't believe the Ark will come, and even if it does she doesn't want to be on it anyway.

In the street Jo and Andy and Dean climb about on the scaffolding of a house which is being renovated, whilst below Polly crashes about on her roller-skates, grinning and gesticulating at the climbers.

'I've told them to come down,' she says, really quite relishing the spectacle.

Across the road Emmaline and her little brothers march off with Trisha, in their best coats. Little Roxana and Jabar play on regardless; they have their own boat coming on another day.

The Ark has arrived. It is moored just round the corner, by the pub, and a procession of folk queue up outside it, waiting for the door to open and the gangplank to go down. Just as it does, The Old Rose opens its doors, and many of the occupants of the queue decide their allegiance lies elsewhere. Some folk don't even see the Ark. Others make rude gestures with splayed fingers. Yet others have brought their swimsuits and prepare to revel in the threatened water. Water is streaming over the pavements already. One voyager, tempted to gesticulate rudely back, is turned off by the others, and makes his way back down the gangplank, to catcalls of triumph from the sneerers below.

Sassy stands on the steps of the pub with folded arms. 'I thought I'd just come and have a look. Oh, look Teeny, there, look! No, I'm not going on it. No, not today, I haven't time. Look at the pretty rainbow . . .'

The child stops howling and glares fiercely into the sky. A rainbow has appeared of beauty and colour so intense that the streets below are radiant and shaking with tints under its broad arch. Two little girls and their barking dog run up and down the street, singing.

The world goes on heedlessly: many haven't even noticed the Ark, they are too busy shopping and playing and looking at each other and, even though their feet are starting to get wet, they don't care. In other parts of the town a good trade is being done in wetsuits and catamarans and the like.

The Ark starts to move, slowly. The children dotted on the scaffolding call, Jo shrieks as she waves and nearly loses her balance. Dale shouts rude words, and cracks into laughter, which echoes about. The inmates of the Ark gaze back over the side, some pityingly. Something funny has happened to them. They have gone flat, like pieces of paper.

The Ark is on the edge of the horizon now, its destination the heartlessness of perfection. Most of the inmates already know what they are going to find – endless fruit, endless harmony, endless entropy, endless endless compassion, black and white in endless inane tableaux of equality. It sails off to a perfect world; the sky has turned into rich primary colours and in the distance the Ark bobs about on a bright blue sea.

Below lie the streets, their corners and rough edges and pitted pavements prisming and splintering the rainbow's light into thousands and millions more lights, making the streets a thousand and million times more beautiful.

Down the main road speeds a figure in worn sandals and a beard. He pauses to look up at the dove circling about his head, and turns in at The Old Rose.

IN THE STREET

THE STREET IS astir: a little knot of children move backwards and forwards over the pavement and road, shouting and arguing. Under all the voices is a harsh gravelly roar. It's Dean.

'They all pick on me,' he bellows.

'No they don't.' (They do.) But he has turned, grabbed the bike from Andy, and ridden off, cackling with laughter.

'Don't pick on Dean, you lot.'

'It's because he's dead horrible,' says Jo earnestly. (He is fairly horrible.)

'Well, you still shouldn't pick on him. You'll make him horrible.'

'Do you live here all by yourself? Well, never mind, we'll come and see you sometimes, won't we Polly?' Jo says generously.

Madame Montessori would be proud of her. Children never seem to be at a loss, they are very managing beings.

'Haven't you got any children? Never mind,' she says then, as though this is a great loss, which makes me hoot with mirth. 'We'll come and see you sometimes, and if you're not in we'll sit on your doorstep – we can, can't we?'

Whilst these two are wittering on, Dean has returned with the bike, crept to the gutter whilst the others aren't looking at him, and picked up a handful of gravel, which he suddenly flings in the faces of the other boys. Outcry. Andy moves forward to hit him, but Polly turns and seizes hold of Dean by the dormant hood on his duffel coat and drags him away, bossy but as though claiming him.

Outside in the garden the daffodils look as though they are in a huff: all I can see from my kitchen window are the backs of their bonnets waving and dipping in the wind.

Whan that April with his shoures sote, the droughte of March hath perced to the rote . . . Than longen folk to bomben other folk, as wel in Cristendom as hethenesse . . .

The US Government has dropped bombs on Libya, with British help. Many civilians minding their own business and living their lives have been killed.

The following Saturday there is a meeting in the market square; about four hundred people have turned up just to be there and make their protest at the bombing. It has been arranged very quickly, and all of the placards are home-made and tatty. Petitions are handed about to sign. Speeches are made, and then there is a minute's silence for the victims. A wordless prayer goes up from the small market square, for the people who died far away. Overhead is a peaceful sky and the flapping of pigeons; in the background the distant bus engines. The town clock chimes across the silence, and the speeches continue.

Ahmed has been to a different meeting to protest against the bombing – the mosque out in force.

'There were lots of people there. I held one side of a banner,' he says proudly. 'My brothers and most of my friends came, and lots of neighbours.'

'Did you see Zarina? Was she there?'

Something flickers across his face. 'No, she wasn't, there was no women there. The women have their own demonstration. They don't come to ours.'

He is growing up. I feel as piqued as Titania. 'So, when was the women's demonstration, then?'

He blinks, and looks back at me.

In the street there is bother. Dean has a gashed lip, where he was knocked against the kerb.

'He says it was Andy, and I know Andy, he's my foster-brother, and he would never do such a thing,' says Jo, indignant and definite.

'He did. I saw him,' says Polly.

'They pick on me. They *do* pick on me,' says Dean, throwing himself about.

'When they pick on you, tell Polly. She sticks up for you.'

'Dean, shut up now, and stop being so horrible,' says his suddenly-appointed defender.

Jo has her sleeping-bag tucked under one arm, for it is Friday and she lives somewhere else at the weekend. In the other hand she is carrying a letter. It's from Andy to a girl.

'It's got a heart inside it,' she says importantly.

'It's a bit late for St Valentine.'

She shrugs. 'Doesn't matter.'

The package is handed about among the children and exclaimed over, turned about and examined: 'TO YVONDE'.

'Spelt it wrong,' criticises Polly, over Jo's shoulder.

'That's the way he spells it,' Jo says proudly.

Dean starts howling again. His lip looks very sore. He is a truculent little body of eight years, with a hoarse musical voice. An only child, he doesn't share anything, and is evidently used to being the centre of attention. He has the loudest voice in the street: when he calls across the road the children nearby stick their fingers in their ears and grin. Dean seems to thrive on the antagonism of other children, yet it must hurt him too. He mostly has a wild gleeful expression, hoarse, foghorn laughter. He would rather suffer than be ignored.

'I'm a half-caste,' he barks at the others truculently, flinging wide his arms in delight. Then he kicks a plastic cone left by the council workers all the way down the street.

Rosehill Street in late May – the sound of birds and the smell of anise and early summer greenery; movement of the sighing wind. Here comes Tazilim, hurrying along to Mohammed's, one hand leaden, clutched about her baby, the other makes gay protest at her white chiffon scarf, which whips about her head and shoulders like May ribbons in the warm wind. She passes the green and shushing trees and the girls standing on the corner, and goes her way smiling and untroubled, her mind innocent and quiet.

What a year to be living in – now there is a radiation leak in

Russia. It has been predicted for years, and now it has finally happened. Before the radiation cloud comes I hare off to the supermarket and pile bottles of spa water and lemonade – which is cheaper than the water – into a trolley, as well as bottles of dried milk, and tins of fruit and veg. Leaves no spare money for anything else, but it might be worth it. On the news the government keeps saying there is no danger. Well, I don't believe anything they say. Somehow, none of it seems true, none of it seems quite real. Radiation . . . fall-out . . . for years they have been just words, that's all. There is nothing to show for it. Death-dealing water coming from the taps. More words. Everywhere full of unseen poison, entering our bodies – that can scarcely be believed. Which of us will be struck down? Quite apart from pernicious biological effects, what individual nuttiness is it nurturing? I keep the windows shut, and boil up the cheap lemonade to make tea.

Uggggh.

Zahia is running for the World; he comes round with a sponsor form.

Start out to vote in the local elections, cutting through the arboretum. (This park was a gift to the townspeople from Joseph Strutt, a local benefactor, who believed in the inherent goodness of man.) There is not a single flowerbed left, they have all been turfed over. The sweep of hills and the trees – they can't be touched: it is a conservation area as it was designed by John Claudius Loudon. But the avenues of limes surrounding the green have been ruined. There are now big metal cages dumped on the green, which for years has been a stretch of grass where children came and played and went away again, leaving it intact and empty. The lime avenues are quite spoilt. Go home without bothering to vote.

It's June, but awful, wet and windy and cold. England has had two doses of the radiation, thanks to the lousy English weather – the wind blew the radiation cloud back again, and the rain fetched it down to earth. Thanks, God.

The smell of anise comes strong as I turn the second corner, from the big rowan tree over the wall, and the sound of a cockerel crowing echoes about the streets, its time-mechanism gone amiss. Bump into Jenny at the corner, trying to keep up with her speeding three year old, running from nursery-school to meet the dog. Their dog, Reuben, follows Jenny's two little girls about, and goes delirious with happiness when they come from school; each day he rushes panting through the streets to meet them.

It's Saturday and I'm shoving my trolley about in the super-market.

'Carol!'

I look aside, at a face I hardly seem to know, and yet I do. It's Zarina! I can't believe it. Little Zarina. She has grown tall now. She is wearing Benazir Bhutto-type spectacles and is in charge of a shopping trolley.

'Yes, everyone is well at home. Shamuna? Yes, she's well. She's still the same, still . . . er . . . difficult.' We laugh. 'You must come round. Shabina's had another baby – you must see her, she's absolutely the best of the lot.'

I laugh. 'You said that last time.'

'No, this one really is, I promise you, you'll love her . . .'

Zarina is coming to the end of her O-levels. The last one – Friday the thirteenth. Assorted laughter and eyes lifted to heaven in mock-anguish. Next year, she says, she will be taking history and English literature and Urdu, all at A-level.

I'm fond of Sassy. She came to see me last week, and left early to go somewhere else. Within five minutes she was back again.

'I don't really know what to do. There's this little baby in a car at the top of the street and it's screaming its head off, and you can't hear a thing. Only if you happened to be looking inside the car would you notice it.' We knock at a few houses.

'Ken,' shouts Sassy to a stray man just passing, 'just go and see if anybody in The Falstaff's left a baby in a car.'

He does as he's told straightaway, with a picked-on look on his face. Car door handles are tried, unsuccessfully. A small collection of people is gathered about the car when the father finally falls out of one of the houses, hurries round and unlocks the car door, sheepishly pats the baby on the head for the benefit of the small crowd silently watching his every movement, and drives off quickly.

Ahmed disappears in the summers, he's off somewhere making dens.

June 11th – the first rose of the year, a small red one, very high up.

June 13th – thinking of Zarina, her final exam.

June 14th – it comes over the wireless that Ian MacGregor has been knighted. My God.

Mr Shaw tells me his grandchildren go to private school now.

'Much better. Well – they say – they say that the black children don't get the attention. Not – *all* true.' He appears anxious to be fair. 'But there's *something* in it.'

The children round here post their crayoned pictures through people's letterboxes. So far I've had a fat yellow lady with a skirt like a house roof being propped up on wide-apart legs, a snarled-up green sun, and a thin house whose sharp roof looks as though it is about to puncture the scarlet cloud floating just above. It's late June, it's boiling hot. Outside in her garden Mrs Holmes clinks teacups. Gail and Mike have gone to Skeggy.

In the warm nights cats get on the roofs. At twelve o'clock a cat walks up and down the roofs, yeowling, and lights go on all along the back bedrooms as she moves. Somebody puts their head out. I can't see who it is, but it's Surinder's voice.

'Hello? Ohhhh,' she says sorrowfully. 'I thought it was my Maurice. He still hasn't come back . . .'

Late at night now Joc-wi'-no-fingers is back again; the street lies listening to him through all the open bedroom windows.

'Can yuh hear me, blacks? . . . We fought for yuh. Youse didn't feyt for us . . .'

Oh Lord. His voice sounds hoarser and more chesty since last year; it seems it will get more and more crackly, like an old wireless set, and finally fade into meaningless crackles.

In the warm street Reuben sleeps all night now, in a peaceful heap.

After cashing my Giro at the post office and buying some stamps, I cross the road and make my way round the back of The Old Rose, to see Sassy. She is sorting old photographs for Peter to take to the children's home.

'You see, they're coming up with these new ideas all the

time. I've got to find him some photos – of us all when he was little – and Susan's going to make up a file for him, and they think it might help him. I don't think he'll be interested in old photographs. Not Peter. But anyway, we can give it a try.'

'There we are. That's Peter.' We look at a snap of Sassy, looking more Bardot than Bardot, with her piled-up hair and mini-skirt, holding a fat infant in a bundle, in front of the arboretum bandstand.

'Oh, the mini – I loved the mini. As soon as I came off duty, I was out of my nurse's uniform and into my mini.'

Sassy and I grew up together, but we hadn't seen one another for a long time until about three years ago, so we are catching up with past news all the time. As teenagers, she was working in a pharmacy, I was working in a shoe shop. We went to a party together and parted under the town clock, as we both dashed for our respective buses home. And that was the last we saw of one another for years and years.

'I was married with a baby by the time I was seventeen. When I was eighteen I started nursing. Well. I'd got my job and my baby, and I thought the world belonged to me. And yet I had no money. I'd got my own little house – only rented and it was ever so tiny – but I loved it. I suppose some people would see that time as being deprived or something, but it wasn't like that for me, because I was in control of my life. My marriage had finished, and that was a relief. On my day off I used to push our Paula in her pram along Rosehill Street, and I thought everything was going for me. I felt as though I'd got it all. I never asked anybody for anything. I made do. If I hadn't got it then I went without. It never bothered me. We always ate properly, but then I didn't buy a lot of expensive furniture. All my furniture was second-hand, but now – the teenagers expect it all new, even when they haven't got a job. But I still feel sorry for them, you see, I think they're trying to press money on people because there's nothing else for them. But then again, those people who haven't got anywhere to live get nothing! It's ridiculous.

'My little house! It was pulled down and it was a dear little house. It was only an ordinary two-up, two-down; there wasn't even a bathroom. We had to have the tin bath down, but I didn't mind, I liked it . . .'

'Oh I know – in front of the fire – lovely. Makes the room smell delicious afterwards. I still like to wash in front of the fire, now.' The years in bedsits have accustomed me to having soap and singing kettle and books always to hand, a light snow of talcum powder over everything and a pubic hair with your bacon and eggs.

'There we are, that's a photo of us in the back with the bath hanging up outside . . . Well, there wasn't much to it, but I loved my little house. Even after we left, you'll laugh at this, you'll think I'm mad – I used to go back to see it, when it was waiting to be pulled down. Sometimes, if I'd been shopping, I used to walk back past it, just to see it. And one time I walked down the street, and pieces of wallpaper blew past me, and I could remember hanging that paper myself in the front room – oh, it did look nice when I'd done it! And I walked down the street and it was like bits of my past being blown about in front of me and ripped up by the wind.

'I hope this does something for Peter. I mean, I worry for him. You don't realise how difficult he can be. It sounds awful, I know, but I don't want him back home at the moment. He only gets into a lot of trouble with those Cane boys . . .'

The Cane brothers – everybody's heard of them. Their gang organises bike thievery: they stole the plate out of the church; they lie in wait to take the small Pakistanis' mosque money from them. It was the Canes who beat up Ahmed, a couple of years ago. I heard on the junior grapevine that Peter was reasonable, he never took more than 15p from each child, and could be knocked down to less, and he gave them time to pay.

'He can be very difficult. The last time he was home and he was due to go back, I packed his suitcase, and Susan came for him. She's his social worker and he likes her, so it wasn't that. But she's only a little bit of a thing, only just out of college or training school, or wherever it is they come from. But she's a nice girl and she means well, so I don't say anything.'

'I know it's the trend to knock social workers now, but I always got on with mine, I always liked them. One of my social workers, she helped me a lot. I said to her one day, "How are your other patients?" sort of taking an interest. And she says, "Oh I get absolutely sick of them. Whatever happens, it's always somebody else's fault. It doesn't matter whether it's the milkpan boiling over or somebody running off with somebody's husband – whatever it is, it's never their fault, they won't take any responsibility for their own actions. *That's* the difference, Carol, between those people who really do grow up and the others who never grow up." And that helped me a lot.'

'Well, this is it. You've got to be prepared to listen to what they say. June – she was my social worker, but I don't have her now, but I always got on with her, she spent a lot of time with me when I needed it. She was very good . . . Anyway, as I was saying. I'd packed Peter's bags and Susan had come for him, and we were all stood there at the bottom of the stairs waiting for him to come down with his case. Of course – what did Peter do? – He opened one of the front bedroom windows, jumped out into the middle of the road with all the traffic belting past – it's a wonder he wasn't killed – and he was off. Nobody clapped eyes on him for four days. I mean, he's very difficult.

'Thinking about my life, it all seems – I don't know.' She laughs. 'We're not badly off now, we're very lucky . . . But it's not so long ago when I wandered the streets with our Teeny and wondered whatever I was going to do. Peter was in the home, and Paula and PJ were in care. But now . . . we've got most things really, and I can afford to treat myself now and again.'

She casts a look about her large living-room, with its beams and dresser and old prints on the wall, and tiny cabinet containing Paula's silver christening spoon, the china coronation cup and saucer and the miners' strike mug, and Sassy's nursing badges.

'I always wanted to nurse, always expected to do that. I suppose with my mother nursing . . .'

We used to walk down the street with Sassy's mother to the bus-stop each evening, the folds of her nurse's apron flashing hard-white between her coat gap as she walked. In her shopping basket she carried magazines and a few boiled sweets for her patients. As we waited with her we sometimes begged to be shown her whistle, as a treat. It hung from her waist, a weighty iron one, conferring authority, to be used to summon aid if any patient got out of hand. (In those days patients were not drugged up to the eyeballs and were more liable to be violent.)

'I've never used it yet,' she had declared proudly, 'and I never intend to.'

'I used to really envy you, being able to stop up as late as you liked.'

She laughs. 'Yes – it never worried me when I was small – you see, I'd be with our Joan or the McCanns. But as I got older it upset me a bit, it disturbed me, being in the house on my own. I thought: Well, I don't want to just sit in here on my own. I was really relieved when I got married. I know I was young – sixteen – but with never having a father . . . getting married – it was like my life was really beginning at last.'

The garden is flush with blossom and it's my birthday; roses and blackberry flowers wind about along the walls. I would never in a hundred years have planted red and orange roses together, but they look wonderful. Each year I loosen the brambles around them and let the roses rear up, higher and higher. Soon the whole garden will be full of them.

Go to the telephone box, but it's broken. Wander slowly back up the Sunday street, and see Mr Shaw. He's waving off his daughter and her baby, in the car.

'It's nice to have grandchildren, it's nice for my wife. She can't see them but she likes to be with them, to have them around her. I have six now – well, I have some more in America,' he says suddenly. 'I haven't been there since the war. But I still hear from them now and again. Not very often,' he chuckles.

'Oh America,' I say vaguely, speaking against the afternoon light. 'I've got a father in America, somewhere.' We stare back at each other.

'Nice place. They write now and then, asking me to go over. But I like it here, and I wouldn't want to leave my wife, not even for a holiday. No, I'd never leave her. America – it can be a good life there, they seem to be doing . . .' He nods encouragingly, which I take to mean well. 'But,' he shakes his head, 'very violent. Violent.' He lifts a finger, as if to check himself, as if to be fair. 'Some good things. There are some good things. Yes. They live well, I think they're happy . . .'

I nod. 'Mmmmm. Yes. Still . . . If this was America, everybody in the street would have a gun.'

We look up and down the sunny Sunday street, and exchange amused and awe-full glances.

It's the royal wedding day – rather wet up here. I go to the local bakery to see if they have any special cakes, but all they have this time is baskets of shortbreads on red plaid. I think I could have become more feeling about it had there been cakes.

Mrs Holmes comes into her garden at tea time. She spent a happy morning watching the television. 'Oh it was beautiful . . .'

'What colour were the bridesmaids' dresses? Pink?'

'Well – no – they weren't pink. More – oyster, I'd say. Very pretty.'

She goes back into the house to fetch the evening paper to show me. If at all possible my Aunty Mavis will describe them as being peach. But this time she says biscuit. Biscuit.

'Biscuit? Well I wouldn't say biscuit . . .' says Sassy, and offers light coral. Pale orange, pale coffee, pastel-pink, sugar-pink, salmon . . . I wonder if they are all talking about the same dresses, as the images are filtered through different televisions, eyesights varying in colour perception, and differing vocabularies.

The beginning of August – lashings of rain outside dislodging more slates; berries fruiting in the garden.

The street is full of playing children. There's a great to-do – Polly and Zahia and Dean are telling the other children they heard a ghost in Granny Gripples's, which is an old empty house into which the children often climb.

'It was going – Deeee-eeeeean. Wheeeeewww. Deee-eean,' says Polly.

'It was, it was,' sings out a delighted Dean, jumping up and down, whilst Zahia coughs into his hand with laughter. This proves to be a Big Story: the children go on about it for weeks.

Jenny left at the beginning of the school holidays, and her little girls play out with their dog. The council has descended and the street is being dug up in two directions, the Gas Board is swapping pipes. On the corner Jo and Dean and Chris stand with their hands in their pockets, slightly disconsolate, waiting whilst Andy has his turn riding the bike. Reuben follows the little girls about as they play and, when they go inside, he snuffles about along the pavement. Pam, the Salvation Army lady, sits out on her doorstep, and two blonde girls further down are playing a guitar and singing with a little cluster of children about them, and Reuben, now wagging his tail. Michelle wanders about with Lee, eighteen months old, stomping about with one leg in plaster. Charles – Mr Czech from across the road – wears a straw hat now. He moves slowly down the street.

'I pinch you, you can't pinch me back, I see a man in a white straw hat . . .'

Further down a Vietnamese girl sits out on her step with her baby, unspeaking but watching.

It's the middle of August. The children seem extra noisy this evening – all this ghost-viewing must have made them rowdy.

About half-past twelve I push the bedroom window wide, to shake the bedcovers. A voice calls across the night.

'Can I have a word with you?' It's Trish, standing on her step. I go down to let her in.

'We wondered if you might have seen anything – two nights running now we've had our tyres let down. It must have happened tonight when the street was full of children, because when Paul went out at nine o'clock, that's when he noticed the flat tyre.'

'I didn't see anything – I wasn't looking, but I did notice they were very noisy.'

'When we went out and asked them, they all said the same thing straightaway – It's Dean, but I don't believe them, because they always blame him.'

Paul and Trisha think it's Chris, because he was seen bending down near the wheel.

'He could have been looking at what another child had already done. Giving him the benefit of the doubt.'

'Yes, he could have been,' she says uncertainly. 'The worst of it is, I'm starting to think the whole street's against us, now. That it could happen two nights running and nobody saw anything!'

'You mustn't think like that – it's quite easy not to notice what they're actually doing.'

'Yes, I don't really think that, it's just . . . sometimes you know . . . I'm trying to pray for whoever's doing it, but I'm finding it a bit difficult. Well, anyway, I don't care about any of them. And as for that Chris . . .'

'He's only six, Trisha.'

'Yes. I know. I feel sorry for him really.' She doesn't sound all that sorry, and I don't blame her. The incident has upset her whole family. Especially as it happens again, the third night.

'Now, Chris, who's letting these car-tyres down? Poor Paul had to walk to work yesterday.'

Chris, a six year old with a large round head and large ears, a little homunculus, his face creased with old lines, pulls down his mouth into a triangle and says nothing.

All the children say the same automatically. 'Dean.'

'Dean.'

'It was Dean,' but you can see in their faces that as they say it was Dean they know it was Chris. Even if it wasn't.

AN EVENING WITH POLLY

POLLY COMES ROUND to show me her organ keyboard and to sing some songs. She is a sturdy, fair child of eleven. She can't read music, she says, but plays by ear.

'Just sing me a tune, and I'll play it for you.'

The organ is one of those flat portable ones which you plug into an electric socket. It can also make the sounds of a saxophone, clarinet, banjo, the human voice, as well as dogs and cats. Any tune played can be switched on to these noises, so you can have dogs barking 'Rule Britannia' or cats calling out Beethoven's Fifth. After the first ten minutes or so spent admiring its qualities and trying out all the noises, she settles into chopsticks, and then 'Amazing Grace', her fingers long and knotted and mobile.

'Everybody likes that one. People always ask for it. I've been playing since I was five. I've always liked doing it. My mother bought me this organ for Christmas. Before that, I had another one, but it wasn't as good as this one.

'There's this girl at the school I'm going to after the holidays, and she can read music and she's going to teach me how to do it, so I'll be able to write it down when I make it up. Listen to this one – we used to sing it at the infants: "The ink is black, the page is white, together we learn to read and write . . ."'

She sways as she sings and plays.

'We used to sing that at St Chad's – oh, I loved it, I did,

because before school started you had breakfast, and there was this big plate of sandwiches, ever so many, and only a few children! Egg and salad-cream sandwiches – my favourite! Do you know how to make them? You have to mash the egg into the salad cream . . .' The memory of these distant plates of food brings an enthusiastic flush to her cheeks.

We sing our way through old favourites of the infants: 'Daisies are our Silver', 'Glad that I Live am I', 'Away in a Manger', before singing on to other hymns.

'What about this one, this is my favourite of all:

> Through our God we have the Victory,
> He will help us love our Enemy,
> We will sing and shout the Victory,
> Christ is King.

'I really love that one. I sing it all the time, sometimes. We sing it at Sunday school. Trisha takes me when she takes Emmaline. I like it there; it's the big Pentecostal church on the main road. They don't sing the same hymns there that we sing at school. It's different, really. Everybody's called brother and sister. Last Sunday,' she laughs and catches her chin in her hand, 'me and Emmaline ran upstairs while they were all having their cups of tea and started fooling about on the organ. I always wanted to try out a big proper one, but it took them all by surprise. They sent up to find out what was going on . . .'

Then she launches into 'Early One Morning' and we have a little bit more of a sing.

'What about you, Carol, what do you like to do? Have you got any hobbies?'

'No, I can't think of any . . .'

'Never mind. Not everybody has hobbies,' she says kindly.

'I've been playing since I was five. I've always liked doing it. I can play the recorder too. I'll bring it round and play for you another time. It's one of the heavy ones, quite complicated to play. I like the sound, but my mother doesn't like it round the house: she says it's too squeaky. She doesn't really understand – I suppose it was when I was learning she didn't like it. She won't let me play at home now. But I can play at my dad's.

He doesn't mind. He taught me to play the drums when I was little. He's a drummer. And he can play the bugle – have you ever played a bugle, Carol? It's quite hard. I played two notes when I was very small. I did it by accident! It's a lovely sound, though, and my dad can play it really well.

'I go to my dad's on Saturdays. Last Saturday he took us round town and we bought a duckling. Aaaaaaaah. We couldn't resist it, poor little thing, it was in this small little box with the rain pouring down all round it, and it just sat there. We felt so sorry for it. It's at my dad's now, quacking all over the place.' She sputters into laughter.

'I can't wait to go there this week and see it again. My dad's got lots of animals. Four dogs – well, one's his girlfriend's but we count it as ours, too – and in the garden there's hens and rabbits . . . Carrie – that's his girlfriend, but she's not there all the time because he likes being with his rabbits – Carrie's musical too, she used to be a country-and-western singer in a pub, and she made up this song, it was about two lovers that loved each other. And she showed it this American singer – I don't know his name, but he was on a tour here – and he liked her song and he said, "If you give that song to me I'll record it and use it, and if it makes any money I'll give it all to you." Carrie didn't know what to do, so she went to a solicitor and he told her don't give it to him. He's not obliged to give you a penny. You've got no claim on it if you give it him. So she never gave it him. She put the song in a box and locked it up.'

'Whatever use is a song in a box?'

'Well, but that's what the solicitor told her to do.'

We sit in silence for a minute, perhaps respectful silence for the dead song, before turning to tea and cake. Then the singing starts up again. Polly tries out one of the tunes I made up, slowly fading on tapes. She adds her own bits. Then she breaks into her favourite hymn again, 'Through our God we have the Victory, He will help us love our Enemy . . .'

'My dad taught me lots of songs. Hymns they were, I think. Like hymns.' She hums experimentally. 'I can't remember. I thought I remembered it when we were singing that other hymn . . .' She la-las a bit more. 'I can't remember, it's a hymn but it's a German song. My dad's got lots of German songs; he taught them to me . . .'

The penny drops. 'Does it go . . .' and I hum the Luther hymn.

'That's it, that's the one, Deutschland something . . . My dad, he doesn't like foreigners, except for the Germans. I think he's a bit . . . well, I suppose you'd say he was, well, racist really, he doesn't like foreigners and he doesn't like coloured people. He used to be always fighting them when he was a teenager. I can't remember it, but he did. If I ask him about it he says he still doesn't like them, but he doesn't fight them. And if,' she pursues, relentlessly intent on etching in a scenario acceptable to her, 'he was to see a Englishman hitting a child – it wouldn't matter if it was a coloured child or a Indian child or anything – even if it was a Englishman doing it – my dad – he'd knock him down. He wouldn't stand for it. He wouldn't.' She shakes her head from side to side.

'He's got this scar on his arm, from going to London a long time ago, and fighting. It was when he was a teenager. It was a big lot of people and they all had banners and then they got to fighting . . .'

'Not a demonstration?'

'Yes, that's it, that's what it was, a demonstration. It was before I was born. Let's see, Michelle's thirteen, and it was when she was a baby. There was two lots of people, and the police were trying to keep them apart . . .'

As she speaks, recalling the demonstration from the memory of another, I remember it myself, from the other side, under the flapping banner 'One Race, the Human Race'. It was during the time when everybody linked arms on demonstrations, in order to rush and break the police lines. This sounds fine, but in a crush it leaves your body unprotected. When I got back home I felt as though I'd been beaten black and blue; I was taking hot baths for nearly a week afterwards.

'. . . the police kept them apart but my dad and his friends got into a fight in the tube with some of the other side. That's when he got the scar. My mum was dead mad with him for going . . .'

Polly's mother is a tiny dark-haired girl who wears black

leathers and rides behind her boyfriend on a very big very noisy motorbike.

'Come on, let's have another song.'

'Listen to this, Carol. My little brother had this comic, *Pepper Street*. It was a little children's comic; I never read it but I made up a tune to go with it, so I called it 'Pepper Street'. Do you want to hear it?'

I nod enthusiastically, and she starts up.

Polly's hairstyles change fairly frequently, for her mother used to be a hairdresser. Michelle, the elder girl, has white-blonde hair and marble skin, but Polly is more rounded, more peach-pink, her auriole augmented by a very little judicious peroxide. Both girls wear their hair in the latest styles, and throughout the summer holiday Polly's hair was teased out into a froth. But this week, ready for the new school term, it has been cut into a short bob, slightly waving over one side. Although she wears a track-suit, with her sturdy limbs and fair hair, just at the moment, she has a passing resemblance to one of those line drawings in old thick-paged school-stories, girls with cropped hair and black legs and gymslips, an embryo Joan England, Head Girl and Hockey Captain.

She finishes playing, and looks up, smiling to catch a smile.

We survey the street, grown dark now, and she starts across the road. Then she turns, remembering her manners.

'Thank you for having me,' she says, with old-fashioned courtesy.

'It's been a pleasure.'

Later, about eleven o'clock, there comes a thudding sound, as Polly and Chris and Zahia and his brothers chase about down the entry into the street, and back again through their open front doors, yelling and jumping about in the night street. One of the older children is holding something high in the air, and the others are all chasing after it.

THE TRIP

AT THE END of the summer I go with Sassy and her daughters, and young Deb who sometimes babysits; we take an early evening train to Matlock Bath. The train is slow and calls at little country stations – Belper, Ambergate; Whatstandwell station, deep in fern under the pines, willow-herb seeding along the track. The train passes under tunnels cut into rock, and the striped railway seats stay printed on to my eyelids. Ever since Victorian times there has been a small train rocking into the countryside, to take visitors to the illuminations.

Outside, the light is going, and the train passes fields of sheep, unearthly bright in the falling gloom. Sassy's husband Jack has taken PJ to visit relations, so we are an all-female party. Dusk has fallen when we get off the train on to the little station, and the evening crackles with woodsmoke and expectation.

Up in the wooded hillsides chimneys smoke. Here below, the small shops are lighted up and open along the strand facing the river. Almost as we watch, night falls suddenly. The stars are out, the little street is packed with people. Many are genuine holidaymakers, staying in the vicinity in tents or caravans; some, like ourselves, are here only for the evening, their state as merrymakers more fleeting: bikers in black leathers, passing hikers in stout shoes and anoraks, families from Cheshire and from Derbyshire. Outside the shops stand big baskets of children's fishing nets, footballs, balloons, facing the chestnut trees across the road.

Squashed in between the rock, Matlock Bath is a street of small shops in the ribbon of main road by the River Derwent, which here is but a strip of water beneath a cliff. At the end of the shops is the Pavilion, where visitors took the spa waters in the eighteenth century.

We go first to the shops. The band plays on in the little wooden bandstand made more minuscule by the cliff rising sheer behind. There is nowhere quite like this place. I have memories stretching back to childhood of weekend afternoons in a tea-shop, staring at windows awash with water, and outside Matlock in the rain with the band playing. We go from shop to shop in the push of people. Sassy is looking for a small wedding present for the son of the landlady of The Crown.

'I don't know what to get, I'm sure. I've been asked to the do, it's tomorrow . . .'

She stands transfixed between a fancy candle in the shape of a wedding cake, and a pot kitten in a tiny brandy glass.

'I just can't make my mind up. What do you think?' It isn't really a question, just a sound in her ponderings.

Indian silk scarves, dolls' wooden cribs from Poland, etchings of Victorian Matlock; hand-thrown pottery, pottery seconds, corn dollies, brasses, Kendal mint-cake, for the walkers. I feel festal in a white cotton top, embroidered with white flowers – £2.99. Sassy tries on a pale pink cotton dress, wonderfully loose and drop-waisted, for £10. 'I'm very tempted.' Deb buys sweets, and Teeny, who is five and has hair she can sit on, requests a cow's moo that she can keep in her pocket.

All around, the breathing hillsides, and over us stand the rocks and craggy tors which protect the little basin of celebrating humanity. Doddering about in the darkness are the lights, fitful in the juddering black water. The tiny funfair with its tinny music; fairylights shining and fairylights breaking to bits in the water – some little pieces of children's magic, gew-gaws against the surrounding night.

Paula buys a broomstick; it just takes her fancy – a real besom made with twigs.

'It'll come in handy for Hallowe'en. I've always wanted one.'

She trails it behind her as we wander about the noisy lighted street.

We hang over the water. Cold rises up. Here come the floats, fragile like our expectations. Entirely made of lights, a miniature Venetian gondola, glimmering and sliding towards us, silent, and then lapping as it gets nearer and you can hear the sound of the unseen oarsmen. Behind the gondola, a church, wavering in the water and almost toppling. The sounds of gaiety are frail, muffled in by the black protecting silence up and beyond the street and the water, in the forested hillsides.

Next comes a helicopter, and then the cleverest float – a sea-lion twizzling a ball – the ball's spin an illusion of patterned lights rippling on and off. Here comes a whirligig with sparkling dancing horses: up and down, round and round. Last of all and late, a clock, with its lighted hand speeding madly through the hours. As they circle together there is no darkness; the water here is a burning mass of colours.

We cross back along the bridge, and move towards the shops again. We aren't satisfied until sitting in a place in the grassy rock, picking from parcels of fish and chips. In this little sheltered place we can rest and watch the teeming street.

Sassy smiles indulgently as Paula says gaily, 'Here we are, we're just right – we're all set up, aren't we? All we need now is a man.'

Her bright words hang in the air and turn melancholy. Deb, twelve, chews away unseeing, unspeaking, enclosed in her own world. Now the corners of Paula's mouth are turned down, and the lights shattering in the water suffer another refraction in suddenly prickling eyes. Already, fallen leaves bat about; the wind is chill. It will soon be winter.

'Come on. We'd better get some sweets to take back for PJ, and some rock for Peter,' says Sassy.

Suddenly in the small sweetshop Teeny lets out such a bellow, 'Aaaaaaaagh.'

Sassy flies up into a child's temper herself. 'You're not. You're not and you can just shut up that noise. You don't want one of those horrible things . . .'

'. . . aaaaaagggggghhhhh . . .'

Taking pity on everybody else's ear-drums, Sassy gives way and purchases a pink candy bum on a stick, handing it to the now smirking Teeny. Candy dummies, gnashing candy dentures, disembodied female legs, feeding bottles, bulbous red candy lips – all hang from mobiles on the ceiling, waiting to be picked out of the air by customers.

We sit in the pub yard with glasses of shandy. Deb sits slowly sucking rock, as though in a trance. I lean back against the cold iron chair.

'I think I ought to go back and get that dress,' witters Sassy.

Paula has parked her broomstick against the pub table near her drink and gone off to look at black leathers. In the distance the band is playing 'I Can't Help Falling in Love with You'. Beer glasses clink, and each time the pub door is swung open comes the juke-box thump of Heavy Metal.

Shall we go to Cromford, to the bookshop? It will be closed now, but they leave racks of second-hand books outside all night, and you choose one and post your 20p through the letterbox. It's about a mile away, and we could catch the return train from there.

'Won't Teeny get too tired?'

'*She* won't get tired, my children never get tired, I don't know what's the matter with them. Last week we went to Stenson Bubble all afternoon, and walked about four miles back home, but when I went upstairs at two o'clock in the morning they were still bouncing out of their beds like kellies.'

Slowly we walk the street. Between the rock, Matlock Bath is still small, a village, and in spite of the commercialism, the pinkness of candyfloss and the gaudy lights, the candy bottoms and the empty plastic cups rolling about in the wind with fluttering paper leaves, it has a delicacy which has never been destroyed.

We leave the noise for the road: the lights fondant in the water and smaller and smaller; the tinny roundabout music tinkles into nothing. The road is silent – sky-high black trees ranked on either side. In the spring these woods are heavy with the smell of the pretty white garlic flower which grows in profusion here.

'I don't get a lot of spare time now, but our Paula's always reading books, aren't you, Paula?'

We fritter out into the road to let a couple of cars pass, and re-form again. Paula nods in the wake of the car-lights.

'Yes. Anything. I like books about the occult, or what's happening to the planet. Or science fiction – I hope they have some science fiction when we get there. Or anything really. I don't mind,' she says agreeably. 'I read this story last week . . .'

We seem to have been walking some time, when suddenly between the waving night-firs are rows of dotted lights – Arkwright's factory, its red brick masked now; we see rows and rows of lighted squares and a tall chimney, set back from the road and surrounded by woods.

'Seems a funny place to put a factory, doesn't it?' says Paula.

'Well, I suppose it does,' says Sassy, 'but lots of them were in little places at one time. My mother grew up in a village where everybody worked at the mill, and that's all part of Manchester now, but it didn't used to be. It was a proper little village, everybody knew everybody. As you know,' continues Sassy, preparing to start her story by striking a tiny flame for her cigarette and briefly bringing into being our faces, haloed and warm and bright-eyed.

'As you know, my mam had me when she was in the change, so she was a child at the beginning of the century. Did you know she was the only survivor out of seven little girls? She was. They lived in the house next to the mill, and next door lived her cousins – five little girls and their parents – they had the same surname as my mam. One evening, when she was a baby, she was put down to rest on the settee with her sister, who was about four, nearby. About seven o'clock that evening there was this almighty noise and the mill chimney collapsed and fell on the houses, and everybody was killed. But the settee had tipped up over my mother and protected her, and she was found alive.

'After that, she was fostered out. It was a Mrs Etherington who took her in – she was a very good woman, she was well known for it. She looked after orphans and she was always going round in the evenings with soup and bread to give to anybody who she thought had gone without. And I bet you,' says Sassy, stopping in the middle of the road, one finger in the air holding up her cigarette and wagging, 'I bet you she's one of the few people left who can remember Nancy Dickybird. Yes. She can. Many's the time my mam's woken up in the morning and found Nancy Dickybird asleep on the settee. You see, this Mrs Eth . . . You've never heard of Nancy Dickybird? Well, Salvation Army people still talk about her; they'd be able to tell you more about her than I can. All I know is, she used to get very drunk in the evenings, and after the pubs shut she'd walk through the streets singing – the most beautiful singing. So she was known as Nancy Dickybird. Everybody safe in their houses would hear her. They'd turn over in their warm beds and say, "There she goes, Nancy Dickybird." Some nights Mrs Etherington would say, "Shshshshshsh, I think I can hear our Nancy coming," and she'd go out and fetch her in, and let her sleep on the settee. But all that was before the Salvation Army got hold of her.'

'I've heard Nan go on about Nancy Dickybird, but I didn't know who she was.'

'Well, now you do.'

'Mum, shut up a bit now, Carol can hardly get a word in edgeways, and poor Deb hasn't opened her mouth all night.'

'Nancy Dickybird,' chants Teeny experimentally, 'Nancy Dickybird, Nancy Dickybird, Nancy D . . .'

Teeny and Deb are striding ahead, Deb still enclosed in her silent crystal world, and she's still eating sweets!

'You know,' says Sassy, 'I should have got that dress. I could always keep it and wear it next summer. Oh dear.'

So we keep going, walking and talking, our thoughts on Nancy Dickybird, singing her way in the darkness.

AJIT'S STORY

AFTER GAIL LEFT, another tenant moved in within a few weeks. Gail's urn of flowers had gone, and the borders around the small oblong of grass were suddenly bare in the middle of summer. I didn't see the new tenants, but from upstairs one day saw the garden had filled up with fuchsias and heathers, small bushes and conifers. The months passed and I caught rare glimpses of an Indian lady with a slight, stooping figure, bent over her plants on sunny mornings. But we didn't meet.

Three months later, in October, Mrs Holmes brought the new tenant round to introduce her. Ajit was an invalid with a young teenage daughter. She dreaded the coming winter, she said, because of her chronic asthma, but the pollen also affected her chest. Her frame was so thin and bent it seemed some days to belong to an old lady. Other times, when she was feeling better, she was as lively as a girl, amusing and chatty.

I go round to see her. Now the weather has changed her bare-boarded front room is full of tubbed bushes, pulled inside out of the wind. Her back sitting-room is simply furnished – a bed-settee against one wall, a divan against the other, cunningly contrived by Ajit and Amrita with milk crates and foam rubber and fresh printed material. A colour television – which they both avidly watch – stands in a corner. Two posters of Sikh gurus are on the walls, and Ajit's knitting bag and her bag of drugs (which she must have always with her) rest against the settee. There are days when the bed-settee is pulled right out and she is in bed, wrapped high to the neck in a woolly, the rest of her thin body under a duvet. Although the gas-fire is permanently on and the room is well heated, she is unable to get warm. She lies with exhausted eyes, her hair down in a lifeless snake against her neck.

But today she is fine. Her hair is pinned up, her eyes calm and serene, and she goes to the kitchen to make tea.

'How is Amrita?'

'She is tired, but she is well. There is always homework, and when I am not well she has to do the shopping and the washing. She is so good. At school now her friends are into some new thing. She keeps begging to be allowed to do this thing with the glass, asking the spirits questions. I do not like . . . "Oh, Mummy, please. Everybody at school does it, it's only fun." Ajit shakes her head adamantly. 'I tell her no. You must not do it. It starts in fun, but it is real. I try to make her see that. I believe these things, talking to spirits; magic. Do you believe in magic, Carol?' She laughs. 'I do. Oh yes. My younger sister did this thing with the glass and she did not come out of it for months . . .'

As she speaks and fills the cups, I look outside, beyond the window, where more plants are being made ragged by the wind. She comes in with the scented tea, and we make ourselves comfortable in the cushions.

'Many people here do not believe in spirits. Well, I tell you, I have seen many times examples of this thing. Many times.'

I look at her and she smiles and nods.

'When I was a student in India I went in the holidays to visit my father's eldest sister, to pay my respects. She was older than my father – my father was her baby brother! So she was quite an old lady then.

'She had had seven daughters. This was unusual in India in those days, most people killed them after the first one or two, because they were an expense with nothing to show for it. But my grandfather was a very good man; he promised for the first two daughters – "No, keep her, and I will provide." After the first two daughters my auntie had a son. Her husband's father had married twice – it was the custom in those days if you could afford it – so she had two mothers-in-law. With all the daughters and the two mothers-in-law, this house had always been full of women.

'But the summer I went to stay with my auntie, none of them were there any longer. The mothers-in-law had both died and all the daughters were married. I thought: Maybe this is the last time I see my auntie, for she was quite old.

'They lived in a village further into the plains, so I had to travel a good while on the train. As well as my cases, I took with me food, and my sketch-book and loom, for I was taking fine arts and wanted to keep up with my work during the holidays. It was a small loom, but it was still an inconvenience. From the station I caught a bus – full up, full of people, full of dust, and all the jumping, to give tummy-ache! Oh, it is terrible! You ache all over, there are no sponges on the seats. My friends at college, we used to sit on our books, but I did not like to do this alone because always there are those elderly people on this country bus and they call out, "Shame on *you*! Shame on *you*!" They think if it is a book you should respect it.

'As soon as I arrived at the house I dropped my cases, and there was my auntie's dog, Honey, waiting to shake hands with me.

'In the houses in India there are always visitors, and my auntie had staying with her her grandson, who was my age. Bobby was a student too, although afterwards he became a farmer. That is quite usual with our people; they get a degree in medicine or engineering, and afterwards they farm.

'The only other people in the house were my auntie's husband (he too was old; he was retired by this time, but he had been the District Commissioner so he was still often called away on business to settle local disputes and that kind of thing) and two Muslim girls who had been with the family since Partition. As small children my uncle had taken them into his house during the trouble, and they stayed. They were like part of the family. Everybody loved them and looked after them, and they were treated as one of us, except they worked in the kitchens and we did our studies. They lived there as children, and when they grew up my uncle found husbands for them, and gave them dowries. To the elder girl he gave four hundred rupees and cloth and kitchen things. He asked them, "Do you want husbands from your own people, or boys from the village?" They said, "We will do whatever you wish; you have been so good to us, you decide." So he thought it best to find them Muslim husbands, so there would be no trouble. He asked among the local people, and he solved the problem at one go – he found two brothers! So it was just right! They married, and afterwards they still came back to visit the house. They are like family. They still visit now, although my auntie has been dead a long while.

'But this was all afterwards. The summer I visited they were still there. So there were four of us young ones in the house.

'At breakfast, Bobby teased me, because I had just then started being a vegetarian, and to eat meat: no, I still can't. To live by eating another living creature – no.

'"Come on, Seema Didi, eat something, you are too thin." He had such a big appetite. He hunted, which I hated, but we got on well; I liked him, apart from that. In the mornings I helped my auntie, or I went with Tazim to help carry food to the people working in the fields. It is a big job, the cooking. Tazim and Nazim were strong, about fifteen and sixteen, and like beauty queens with all the make-up and the gold jewellery and embroidered clothes. Everybody respected them and they were expected to behave as we did. All unmarried girls in the household have the same protection – it is a matter of respect. While Tazim opened the food, I took my charcoal and pad and went to sketch the place where the cattle drank.

'Most afternoons I worked at my weaving if we did not go to the village. In the evening Tazim and Nazim were fetching in the washing, and Honey made off with a sheet, so there was a chase about the courtyard. He was a big dog, a guard dog, yes, an Alsatian. People in India call their dogs after the dogs in films, and there was a famous dog just then called Honey. So everywhere you went, the dogs were called Honey. Honey was friendly, but I was scared of him. He was not like my little Gary at home – why do you laugh? I could pick Gary up, he was only as big as a cat. He came when I called him, and he hid in my clothes. I had him for years, I will show you a photograph . . . But Honey – no. I was scared of him. Every evening he was let loose to go round the house, before the doors were locked, to make sure there were no intruders.'

'There was a story in the village, everybody knew of it. When my auntie first married, the mothers-in-law had told her of it, and what she must do. There was a tradition, and it was still kept. Many years before, not in anybody's lifetime, nobody could remember it, there had been a big dispute over land, and there was fighting and bloodshed, much terrible bloodshed. Many Muslim people were killed in the village, and in the house too, including two babies, twins. Ever since that time, one door of the house had always been left unlocked. If this was not done, the Babies cried. Many people in the village had seen them.

'It was the custom in the house for the last one who went to bed to lock all the doors, except for this one door. It was said that if the last one locked this door, the Babies would be angry and knock, and that person would see them. It was the tradition, but no one had done it for a long time, although many people claimed to have seen them. Still, we young ones wanted to see for ourselves. So we had a pact. We arranged that each, in turn, would be the last to close the doors and at the end of four days we would compare notes. But before that time, we would not speak of it again.

'Bobby was the first to go. He had to wait until everyone went to bed. My auntie went first, she was tired. Tazim and Nazim were in the corner, making cotton into swabs for the lamp wicks. Bobby kept yawning – great yawns, to make my uncle feel tired, which made us want to laugh. But all that happened was my uncle fell asleep in his chair. Bobby then said in a loud voice, "*Bedtime*," and he stretched and smiled at me; and Tazim, who was trimming the big lamp, smiled too, behind the head of my uncle, nodding over his paper. She set the glass chimney back on the lamp; this was my uncle's lamp, the rest of the household each had a *deva* – little clay lamps like dishes, filled with oil. Eventually (oh, what a long time it seemed!) my uncle got out of his chair, collected his lamp and wished us a good night.

'The next morning, when I went to breakfast, Bobby had gone off early to visit a dam, and he was away all day. The afternoon

I spent weaving my rug. The weather was going to change soon. Outside in the trees the peacocks were shrieking more loudly than usual: kee-*yah*-koh, kee-*yah*-koh . . . They always give a sign of storm; they are such sensitive creatures. They gave a sign before China made bomb raid. Kee-*yah*-koh, kee-*yah*-koh . . .

'My turn was second. After they had all gone to bed, I took my *deva* and the house keys from a nail in the porch, and I walked about the house, locking all the doors, going from room to room, with Honey leaping about in front of me and worrying me a good deal. I walked the length of the building, locking the verandah windows one by one. The house consisted of two square buildings, laid bottom tip to top tip, like a flat figure eight, or two diamond shapes. On the verandah of the second building we laid out our beds in the summer months.

'From the village I could hear singing, and the little boys, the shepherd boys, playing their flutes, remembering the god. It is singing but it is worshipping. We call it *arti*. Nearby, I heard crickets, and when I lifted the lamp I could see where the kunda tree shone across the courtyard in the dusk, with its white flowers and wonderful scent. I crossed to the other building and made for the last door, which was right at the join of the buildings. It opened into an empty grain store. It had not been used for keeping grain for a long time, and nothing much was there except old farm tools, and spare sacks.

'Honey stopped when we came to the old grain store – he knew that it must not be locked, and he stayed outside barking when I went inside. There was no key for this door, so I took the old lock on the door and bolted it across, and turned to leave. Honey barked outside, and the door started shaking.

'They banged, they screamed, they hit the outside door chains up and down, oh, my God! I went out by the next door and there they were. They were so beautiful. Baby boys, exactly the same. Such beautiful children, Muslim babies, between one and two years old. Their bodies were naked and pure white, and they had fair hair and blue eyes. Yes, Carol, they do have that thing. In our part of the world it is quite common to see Muslim children with blue eyes. So beautiful.

'I saw them as I see you now, sitting there. No, nobody ever saw them playing. They were only seen when they were angry. I took my bed and rolled it out on the verandah, but it was difficult to sleep. Thousands of stars – yes, they are brighter in India; how do you know that? They are different stars too, I think, and there seem to be more of them: the sky is full of stars. I kept thinking of the Babies, how angry they were. Their eyes were furious and they were in such a temper – like a baby does have, but it can be frightening, to see a baby in a fury. When eventually I fell asleep I dreamed of the Babies; They came again and They were as high as the sky and They were still angry and crying, and beating at the door. It was a bad dream and yet it was wonderful to see Them.

'The next morning at breakfast Bobby smiled at me, and so did Tazim. Tazim was laughing, so I think she had already seen the Babies but had not wished to say.

' "Come on," said Bobby, "eat something. I made a good catch on the way home yesterday. You are too small and thin, put some flesh on . . ." Tazim laughed, her gold earrings shook. They both seemed to be in the know. My auntie knew what we were doing, she had had bad dreams and headaches, and she was very angry.

' "Who is locking out the Babies?" Oh yes, she scolded us well!

'A few years later I went back to say goodbye, just before coming to England. My auntie was an old lady, and I knew I would not see her again. Bobby was not there, he was away in America, and Tazim and Nazim were married.

'The house was being rebuilt, the daughters and their husbands wanted it to look more the thing, to be more in fashion. It looked quite different; they were using new bricks, oh, not like the old ones. The old bricks were like Weetabix, and the mortar, it was a pinkish colour – you do not see it now. You see it sometimes in pictures in old books, but not any more. It has all gone. The builders were using ordinary cement that you see anywhere. But my auntie would not let them pull down the old grain store where the Babies came in. Oh no. That part was all still the same. The Babies were the luck of the house. My auntie had been told this by the mothers-in-law.'

'I did not know what was waiting for me in England, apart from a husband, but I was excited, I was happy to go. We were a close family, I love them, but I had already lived away from home at college, so it was not such a pull for me as it is for many of our girls. But I was going to another country and I did not know what was waiting for me.

'Well, I was cheated . . . Eventually my health gave way, after all those years alone in damp rooms, with no money and no relations here. At first I was at university, studying law. But my husband's relations made things difficult, so I gave it up. I had to fight to get my baby back. She was five years old before I could take her. My social worker helped me. She said, "I think you've got a good chance of getting her back." She was like a mother to me, she was so good. I started teaching handicrafts in a junior school, and my social worker (she was a good friend now), she let us rent a room in her house. But then she died.

'It is a rude life here in many ways; there is so much loneliness, so many lonely people. In India we used to feel empty if we did not see someone for half a day. And there is no need to be alone there – you can go to people's houses – *Panji*, I am alone, and they understand.

'It was hard at first but it was so wonderful when I had Amrita with me again. It is hard for us now but we manage. There is a lot of prejudice still; we still feel it. When I went down to the fostering unit, they would not look at me. They had been advertising for foster-parents, but the woman I saw said no. She said it was because they wanted two parents. But I don't think it was that. I could sense she did not want to let me have a child.'

'Ajit, however would you cope with a child? You can hardly look after yourself when you're ill.'

'No, if you train a child well, it is no trouble. It is all in the training. You can train a child to do as it is told, and it is no trouble. It does as you tell it.'

'But children shouldn't do as they're told.'

She sighs, and then smiles. 'Well, Carol, we will never agree about this thing.'

The front door slams. It will be Amrita, back from school. She comes through, casts an amused hello at us, and slings her satchel into the corner. Then she goes into the kitchen to make a drink.

It is time to go. We make our way to the door through the rescued bower in the front room. Outside the street is darkening; the paper-boy passes with his sack. Beyond the rooftops the sky is already busy with evening clouds jostling the bits of day, and a piece of far turquoise where Venus makes an early sparkle. We say goodbye; a door closing and another door closing sounds in the street as we each return to our private worlds.

ROUND AND ABOUT

IT'S SEPTEMBER, IT'S blackberry crumble time again. Out there in all the brambles the garden is full of fat birds come for berries and hips. Two of them are on the wall now, plump and tipsy.

I'm still signing on. Endlessly – although I don't mind really. Outside the labour exchange a couple of small beeches are just turning, the gold piling up at their feet. Today the signing clerk is a mild punk with a cold. He nods affably. I scan the wide room for Kay. She hasn't been around for a year now, she seems to have disappeared – perhaps moved or got a job. The people signing on that I feel most sorry for are the men who have obviously worked all their lives, and suddenly found themselves out of a job. You can tell from their faces that it really hurts to come here, it's shaming. It would be no use writing 'AT LAST – IDLESSE' on the labour exchange walls (something I've been meaning to do for ages) because they don't feel that way about it. Only the other week a man just into his fifties, made redundant from the railway, dropped dead from a heart attack at the Social Security offices. The worry and upset of all the rigmarole, losing his job and then not getting dole for six weeks, killed him.

In the streets the road is still being mended, red and white plastic ribbon drifting about like bunting, red and white wooden crash barriers propped against gaping holes. Pam, the Salvation

Army lady, is out every morning with her walking stick. In one year she has become disabled.

'I've got to keep going, darling, I've got to *make* myself . . .'

Gail and Mike have left, Polly and family are leaving. Jenny ran off with a sailor and still hasn't come back. Her little girls are well looked after, clean dresses on every day and their hair brushed. They still have their dog, he follows them about, and they are hanging on to their long hair.

It's a year since the Brixton riots. There have been more riots, I think they said on the wireless. I didn't listen much this time. Nobody that I know of flutters an eyelash about them round here. Nobody mentions them. Second time round, I suppose.

The swing in next door's back is roped up and tied to its frame, as it has been all summer. The Shaws' grandchildren are rarely seen now.

'Lita doesn't play with us any more,' says Roxana mournfully. The only girl in a family of four, she seemed to be a particular fan of the energetic Lita, who was the boss of the yard. But they go to private school now, and don't mix in the street.

There is a knock on the door. It's Jenny's three year old, holding up a finger. 'I've got a plaster.'

In the evenings I can feel myself crackling, full of electricity, full of life and I can't understand a bit of it.

Ahmed turns up at the end of the summer. He's grown.

'Hello, stranger. Where are your crutches?'

This is the first summer holiday for ages that he hasn't broken a leg; three years running he turned up on crutches. One time he fell down a drain. Last year he didn't actually break the leg, just slashed it up a lot falling off a roof, but Casualty gave him crutches anyway, to keep him happy.

Here comes Sassy, pushing a trolley home. 'I've just been stopped and told not to take the trolley out. I said, "All right then, are you going to deliver?" That shut him up.'

What would we do without trolleys? I keep groceries in a trolley, until it's time to push it back to the supermarket and fill it up again. There's even a small one in the bedroom – handy to just drop stuff into and drape discarded garments about its sides. Once you start using them you wonder how you managed before. Sassy piles clean clothes awaiting the iron in one, and throws the children's toys in another. The lady over the way uses one for holding her wet washing as she pegs it out, pulling it after her down the garden path. When the cat broke his leg, after the vet had set and pinned it, I put him in a trolley with a blanket and the ironing board on top, and there he sat, absolutely furious, but he couldn't get out.

Cash my Giro at the post office, then cross the road and go into the second-hand shop. You can get some really good things. Coming here is like being let loose in somebody's attic. You have to be canny, though, because you can easily get a bargain that's no good to you. Like a silver evening dress for £3.50 – just the thing for going to the labour exchange in. Bump into Trisha; she's going through the children's clothes rail with the speed and sharp eye of a busy mother. Small James has got lost under the blouse rail.

'Look at this, what do you think?' She has pulled out a linen dress, and we exclaim over it.

The lady behind the counter is folding scarves.

'When I first started here (it's all voluntary, you know, we don't get paid) I told my son, and he said, "Oh no, you're not. You're not going there. It's not safe." And he should know, he's a policeman. I said to him, "It's only at the very top of Rosehill, it's before you get to Rosehill Street." So he said, "Well, all right then, but I don't like it."'

'Why? Whatever did he think was going to happen to you?'

'I don't know, but he *is* a policeman, so he knows what he's talking about.'

This area is called many names: Rosehill, Peartree, Normanton. My favourite is Litchurch, but this isn't used so often now. The areas all merge into one another here and there, and it's good not to have a precise name, it's like the life here is still escaping. I'll hate it if any of the names become official, to the exclusion of the others.

When the children are at school an almost turn-of-the-century quiet lies along Rosehill Street, with its villas and greenery. After the Pentecostal church (redbrick Victorian, square stained-glass windows, pigeon-decorated dome on a little turret) is the mosque, white in the sunshine. A few small shops are dotted here and there between terraced houses, and small pubs. The doctor's house stands on a corner, with gables and angles and ranks of tall chimneys, three by three. Next to it stands the house where the music teacher used to live: Miss Susie Frearson, Piano and Singing. Mrs Holmes can remember her; as a little girl she went for lessons. 'Lift your head up, Evelyn. Open your mouth . . . now, one, two, three . . .'

Rose Villa, Myrtle Villa, Dovedale Villa, Rydal House. Me and Ahmed found some old postcards on a market-stall, from the Great War front, addressed to Miss A. Coombes, Overdale Villa, Rosehill Street. We scurry along, examining the houses, but can't find Overdale Villa. Did he die, the soldier? Probably. There is no writing on any of the cards, but on the front of one of them she has written, in slanty black ink, 'It's man's duty to die for his country, and woman's to die of grief'. Mrs Holmes is consulted, but she doesn't know where Overdale Villa is sited.

'Oh, wait a minute. Miss Coombes. That'll be Miss Ada Coombes (Ada! Oh and I wanted it to be Ann) . . . I can remember her well; the family kept a shop. She never married; she was a typical spinster, as you might say . . . but I never knew she had a Past.'

Then she says tartly, 'I don't think I should like my private correspondence to be on a market-stall for everybody to come and look at.'

Past several streets of rubble there's the school – a Victorian church school, rescued from demolition and turned into a community centre. And across the road is the shop where we used to take the swill-pail from the school dinner-table. It was kept by two old ladies, tall and thin, with buns and sharp noses. They kept hens and a pig in the back, and when you handed over the swill-pail they gave you a penny chew from mittened fingers. The shelf in the shop window was lined with newspaper, with an assortment of children's sweets laid out: barley-sugar twists, refreshers, black-jacks, sherbet-dabs, liquorice catherine-wheels, cinder toffee, chocolate dates, sweet peanuts. And the chews: banana-splits, rhubarb-and-custard, fruit salad. Inside in bottles were coltsfoot rock and tigernuts, and lemon *kali* to take the roof of your mouth off, as well as bronchial drops for the elderly. In the other window were piles

of small sixpenny bundles of firewood. Up until only a few years
ago one of these old ladies was still there in the shop. Her grey
hair had turned white, and she still wore her mittens with the
chapped red finger-ends showing, in summertime too. But she's
gone. It's just an ordinary shop now.

There's the house where the school mistress used to live with
her friend: Miss Morley and Miss Washington. (Miss Prune and
Miss Prism, behind their dusty laurel bushes and stained glass
vestibule.) Miss Morley refused to speak to my mother when
she was a teenage girl and pregnant with me, because she
wasn't married. This seems quaint now, but it probably wasn't
too delightfully quaint at the time. The laurels have gone, and
six-year-old Shafina swings on the front gate.

Anything round here wandering about wearing high-heels and
swinging a shoulder-bag is assumed to be for sale, but then . . .
that happens anywhere, and usually in a far less clear-cut and
so more confusing way. As Sassy says, 'I've lived round here
all my life, and I'm not going to stop walking down the streets.'
Here is the wide front garden, well set back, where the vicar's
sister used to hold summer tea-parties. The drive was gateless,
yet no child passed the invisible barrier. On our way home from
school we could see them sitting near the house through a
misty net of willow, in their own far away summer.

Now the lawn has been tarmacked for a carpark, and the
gabled house belongs to the social services. The willow is still
there, and the big copper beech is just starting to turn.

All down one side overhangs with trees from the park, and
you can hear birds singing the length of the street.

There it is, in a front garden, the I-Love-You tree. A stiff
black holly tree, left to grow as it will. It used to be shaped
like the Ace of Spades with its base high off the ground. I was
seven, and returning from school with Susan, when a piece of
paper fluttered out of the tree like a falling leaf. We dashed
forward, and I picked it up. 'I Love You' was inked on it. I
was thrilled to bits. 'Oooooo,' said Susan, as though she knew
all about it, 'this must be the I-Love-You tree.'

I took the piece of paper home. How long had it been in the
tree? Was it for somebody special? Was it for me? It was for me,
I knew that, and it was from the tree, and yet . . . from another

person. But more than that. I didn't know where it was from. It was a matter too big for me to understand. I held the snip of paper and felt warmed by its message. Once home, I took another piece of paper, and wrote 'I Love You' on it. The next morning Susan and I stood underneath the dense dusty black where the holly formed a round ceiling for us, and shelter when it rained. I reached up and pushed the paper into the prickly darkness of the tree, for somebody to find. It was my message to them. I didn't know who was going to find it but, whoever it was, the words were still true. I meant them, just as an unknown person had meant them for me. We hurried off so as not to be late for school, and I carried with me a big overwhelming in the chest, almost too much for me to manage.

After then, I sometimes looked for another message, but there was none. The words had been said, and you couldn't say anything else. The tree stood, a mystery, and that was that. It stayed the same, it never changed, winter or summer. About seven years afterwards Carole Ann and myself were wandering down the street in our jeans, worn that summer rolled nearly to the knees, and neck-scarves knotted to one side. We walked purposelessly, half-looking for the boys who rode along here on their bikes, half-looking for girls. A little jibbering swarm of juniors buzzed excitedly under the tree.

'Look at them,' said Carole Ann. 'One of them must have found something in the I-Love-You tree.' We exchanged amused and superior glances and continued our hopeful stroll.

There it stands. No longer kept trimmed, no longer looking like the Ace of Spades, but massy and overgrown.

Well, we're nearly at the end of the road which widens where the carriages used to turn in the early part of the century and slopes downwards three ways. Many of the street signs leading off Rosehill Street have been painted over green and gold and red, the colours of land, of heaven and of blood. In spite of headlines now and then in the local paper – vice area this, red light district that – it's quiet here at nights, too. There's no neon around, in fact, the street lighting is minimal. There are just family houses, mostly with families in them, and the girls, and the darkness of the arboretum, alive with trees.

After she has put her young children to bed, Trisha comes

here in the evenings, on a coffee run from the Pentecostal church to the waiting girls, telling them about Jesus and how he still loves them.

'Jesus loves you. Whatever happens, he still loves you, and he always will. It's never too late to turn to him. He cares about what happens to you and he's always watching over you. How many sugars?'

The young girl who is shortly to offer herself as a prostitute blinks sooted lashes and lifts tattooed hands to receive the hot paper cup.

'I can't stop long, lovey,' she says soothingly, warningly.

Ahmed and I have just spent a whole half hour of our lifetimes trying to remember the name of the seventh dwarf, and now we are sitting about studying the black and white squares and trying to decide which floor tile, being cleaned, will give the illusion that the whole floor has been cleaned. Ahmed thinks it is the middle one; I think it is the one just off-centre. It may be that there are two which need to be washed, to create the idea of a clean floor. Naturally enough, I have more interest in solving this problem than he does.

'That old silly Father Masham has been writing to the papers saying that women shouldn't be priests,' complains Ahmed.

'Really? I had no idea you held such advanced opinions on the subject.'

He sits in the armchair with his hands folded across his middle, and a satisfied smile, looking as though he has plenty more opinions where that one came from.

'No, but I think Father Masham's wife would do it just as well, don't you? Don't you think she would?' He has had a big opinion of Father Masham's wife ever since she went up to the school and showed them how to make crackers.

'I don't know.'

'What about,' he says then, 'when you were nuts and you thought Father Masham thought you'd pinched the Baby out of the manger?'

'Oh, shut up.' We giggle, and after that I turn slightly irritable.

'I don't see what's so very funny about it. When I was at

school the Baby was in the manger and that's where it stayed. It didn't jump about.'

'Why does it jump about now then?'

'I don't know. Maybe they don't put it in the manger until midnight because that's when Christ was supposed to be born, like some silly-daft Catholic conjuring trick. It's only a doll.'

Ahmed keeps mum but his eyes are alight with pleasure because he likes to see me spit a bit.

'Although, actually,' I add, not liking to be pinned down, 'I think it's a good idea to put it in then . . .'

Then we tell our dreams, like Red Indians do.

'I was crying because my father had just died. Then I got on the back of this goose and it flew away. It flew way up and landed on the moon, and then I walked up a pathway that went right up to the shrine of a god. It was Shiva; he was sitting there with a snake curled round his neck and a trident in his hand, but he was asleep. I said this prayer in Hindi – oh, I forgot to tell you, I think I was a Hindu – and I said this prayer to wake the god. I can't remember it now, but it was real nice. I went round saying it for days afterwards and everybody got sick of it. My mum said, "Are you still going on about that dream?" The prayer was a special prayer to wake the god. But you can only do it if you're very good at saying it, and I was good and it worked, and the god woke up. Then he told me whatever I wanted I could have. He showed me lots of jewellery but I said no. Then he showed me all piles of food – mmmm, grub, plates and plates, all sorts, lovely – and I said no. Then he showed me rich clothes and I said, "No – all I want is my father back." Shiva said, "No." So I started crying again and I said, "I'll do anything, if you can only bring my father back, make him come back from where he is and be back home when I get there," and the god said, "No, I can't do that." I said, "You're no sort of god if you can't bring my father back, who cares about you!" Then I got back on the goose and flew off again.'

'And that was the end?'

'Yes.'

We sit in silence for a while.

'I was in this dark bright sky, and it was the same night that was there between the prayers I used to say in my head as a child. I'd forgotten about it but it was this special deep night in my head with a few stars, that was there after I'd said "Gentle Jesus" and before I'd started on the Lord's Prayer, and it was full of . . . of *feelings* – I can't describe. Anyway, this same night was full of all the Catholics – all the Catholics there ever were, alive and dead – they were there, but you couldn't see them, because this deep night was everywhere, below as well as above – all the Catholics were there, but not with their bodies . . .'

'With their souls,' agrees Ahmed.

'Yes, with their souls. And they were there for ever and always, er . . . sempiternally . . .'

'And the Catholics had passed a resolution, sympathising with the Protestants but gloating over them as well, but not in a nasty way. The resolution sympathised with the Protestants because they (the Catholics) were not so deeply suspicious of every last thing in the universe. Those were the exact words – every last thing in the universe.'

'Hmmmm,' says Ahmed. There's not much more you can say.

After that we have a game of cards.

'I say, what happened about the muezzin? Does it sound now along Rosehill Street?' This has been a headline story in the local papers over the summer, but I haven't followed it closely.

'No, it doesn't. All the English residents ganged up together and signed a petition and stopped it,' he says disgustedly.

'I should think they did. Who wants that noise five times a day?'

Ahmed jumps up and slams his plate of spaghetti down on the table. 'Right. I'm going.'

'Don't be delicate. Who's getting at you?'

'Only joking.' He sits down again. He was joking and he wasn't.

'If Father Masham wanted to ring the church bells five times a day I don't suppose they'd be any better pleased. English people gave their own priests the old heave-ho, you know, so they're not likely to take kindly to your priests jumping up and down.'

'Yes, all right, I heard you. I don't care.'

Then he says, 'Carol, do you ever give your cat spaghetti? If I left a little bit, could I give it to her? Would she eat it? I've never seen a cat eating spaghetti before.'

On my way home from the pictures I pass Lesley and her man, sitting outside the supermarket in the dark, with a bottle. Have they left Mohammed's? They sit with their backs against the dim glass, perhaps staying close to what vestigial light there is in the empty store. I smile a useless smile through the night.

For a while in the summer he walked about alone, looking lost without her, scurrying along with his head bent. Was she ill? Had she left? It was impossible to ask. So she's still around.

In The Mafeking, Gail polishes glasses and smiles as one of the regulars tells her of the time he was stationed in Cyprus.

Trisha says Heather has killed herself. Heather? The girl on the check-out in the chemists. She was seventeen; she lived alone in a flat. She was very friendly at work but never went out at nights.

The bulk of the pub on the corner, with its warm red brick and those windows whose upper panes are divided into little squares, it resembles a ship, and as I walk past it's like it's floating, a big rosy galleon, up in the waves of the sky.

Across the road Ron stands on his doorstep, tasting the air. He is waiting to hear from the hospital, to know whether or not he has a tumour. He sets out to collect a newspaper from the shop, trying to enjoy each moment of not-knowing.

On Tuesday evenings Surinder's small daughter hurries along to her Indian dance class.

'I love Indian classical dance. It takes years to learn, it's very complicated. Go and fetch your ankle-bells to show Carol. She does some of the dances now, but I don't let her wear the make-up. I don't like it on her little face. There's plenty of time for that later on. Wearing the correct make-up is part of the dance. Oh darling, you've lost one of the bells. You must be more careful with your things . . . I love Indian classical music, too. It's so beautiful. Sometimes in the evenings I sit here alone listening and it makes me feel so good, so peaceful.'

I stand at the doorstep arguing with Jehovah's Witnesses about my immortal soul. 'No, I'm sorry, you're wrong. There's nothing in the Bible that says man has an immortal soul.'

He pencils 'EZEKIEL' on a scrap of paper. Well, Ezekiel has his views, but I believe I do have an immortal soul.

Dean brings old newspapers, for the cats. He is well, he is blooming. He is a choirboy now, so isn't around as often as he used to be. Today he is very chatty. I ask him about the let-down tyres in the summer.

'It was Andy,' he says at once. Well, that doesn't surprise me.

'And Polly.'

'Don't tell lies.'

He gets immensely energised by this remark and says with gusto, 'It *was* Polly: Polly's very naughty, she's got this gang – Polly's gang – Zahia and them – and they're always doing naughty things. They even – ' His eyes are getting bigger with the dreadfulness of it all, 'they even broke into a house – Granny Gripples's house – and took a lot of money.'

'But she's dead. It was an empty house.'

He jumps up and down in reply, and bursts out, 'Yes, it's an empty house and they heard a ghost there. And it was saying my name!' He sounds quite indignant about this now. 'And after that Polly found a lot of money, £100, and she gave me £50 . . .'

Lyndsey comes dancing up the street followed by her dancing small sister and the dog. 'I'm playing a tambourine,' she says gaily, twisting a hand and smacking at the empty air.

Mrs Holmes knocks with her walking-stick over the wall at my window. 'Joan's coming in tonight, and we're Scrabbling. Are you coming round?'

In the tiny room we sit at the table, with our lettered tablets and wooden stands. Sally, the glossy black and white cat, lies asleep before the fire. In the corner is a big photograph of Mrs Holmes's son in gown and mortar; Crown Derby plates hang from the walls, and a print of cut azaleas. From a hook near the television hangs the quote from George VI's Christmas broadcast; two little pot kittens wave from a shelf. The table is decked out with the words beans, deeds, smote and shoon, and one ponders whilst the other two exchange chat.

Then it's break time. We sip from the Derby Posies teacups.

Mrs Holmes has made egg-custards, delicately-flavoured and slippery, and powdered with fresh nutmeg. Joan and Mrs Holmes have lived round here for years and years; they are part of a network of ladies who ring one another up and go to each other's houses, and meet to play Scrabble and talk. In its warmth and gentility it's like a little Cranford, yet it exists here.

Mrs Holmes and I stand outside admiring the hunter's moon making pools of blue on the chimnied roofs and bringing alive the gardens and houses.

About half-past twelve I'm shaking the bedcovers free of cat hairs out of the window. A man walks stiffly and slowly from the pub and down the street. He's not singing; in fact, he's barely walking. About half-way down he starts examining each door and window elaborately, perhaps to see if it is the one he is looking for. He taps at a door in a scurried, mouse-like way. Eventually a girl opens it.

'Who do you want?'

He mutters back something that I can't hear.

The girl answers him apologetically. 'I'm sorry . . . I'm sorry, I think you've got the wrong house,' and then quietly closes the door.

The man turns and crosses the road, making off rather jerkily down the street. So he wasn't looking for a real door, not a real door in this street anyway, perhaps not a real door at all. I wonder if he knows where he is. It's a cold night to have nowhere to go.

I draw the curtains against the October night. These curtains with the summer flowers on – Hawa helped me sew them. Well, I wonder how she is. I don't know when I'll see her again.

Trisha has a thing about Hallowe'en, she can't stand it. 'Everybody seems to celebrate Hallowe'en now, I don't know why. The witches are laughing all over their faces when they see people celebrating their festival. The witches just love that. Oh yes,' she says crossly.

From the noises of the road I step through the park gates and into a world of whirling leaves, spinning, spinning. Each day now I come here, now the leaves are on the move, dancing under the blue and brimstone sky of October. Exult O dust and ashes! This autumn arboretum, I have it like a man has a woman, over and over again and I still can't get enough. I go down the paths of the past, walking as an incantation, and all paths meet at the dead fountain.

The arboretum itself can't be touched, but now they are pulling down the outer walls, and so destroying it as a little retreat. Joseph Strutt's big ideas and generous pocket, all the skill and art of Loudon which created the illusion of space and privacy – such a treasure in a densely populated land – have been brought to naught as the park is made open to the streets and revealed as but a few paths and some trees, and the dream is broken.

In the twilight I pass Paula, sauntering along the main road with her broomstick, and Emmaline and Lyndsey in a bunch of twittering little girls, on their way to Brownies, Reuben following behind enthusiastically, tail wagging. Lamps burn in the temple, in preparation for Diwali. That's where Surinder and Hardip go at this time of year. The road is alive with noise and coloured lights and tinsel, glittery pictures of the goddess and Krishna and pretty swinging lanterns. In the Ajanta Café they are playing snooker now; in the warmth the pinball machines whir and spin. Traffic streams past, car lights winking, and amid the decorations the traffic lights seem decorative too, flashing their jewels between the shop windows full of saris and fruit and sweets. Way above, the Edwardian dormer windows look down with dusty long-dead eyes at the razzle below.

I call round to see Mrs Holmes, bent over her latest knitting.

'What a lovely pattern. I haven't seen one like that before.'

'Oh, this is a very old stitch. It used to be called fan-and-feathers.'

There she sits, into her seventies, doing her bit to stop things bright from slipping into oblivion.

'You know,' she says, 'there's something *about* this street . . . there's always been a pleasant atmosphere here. I don't know why our street was saved when so many like it were pulled down . . . But anyway, never mind, we're still here!'

The jobless figures have gone up again. This doesn't seem to have any meaning any more.

So. The year rolls onward to its close. Next week Trisha and I are going to a performance of *Messiah*, and after that Mrs

Holmes will come in for her annual glass of sherry, a ritual drink to wash away all the year's petty annoyances, which are bound to arise between people who have back doors facing across but eight feet of space. In the New Year I'm going on a Re-start course for people who have been out of work for a long time.

It is just before winter. In the garden under an old dislodged slate snail families are piled together in clusters, each fragile whorl curled round with its tiny speck of hope. Today, just at the moment, the future seems full of hope to me, although all around are drugs, Aids, radiation; further afield cavalier bombing of civilians and mass starvation. Still, here we are, in this small island of Britain, where nobody dies of starvation and every two and a half minutes a person tries to kill themselves.

This town is supposed to be a drugs centre but, unless you are directly involved, as you live your life there is no reason to see anything. All last year there was a drugs dealer living just across the street, but I didn't know until my Aunty Mavis told me about it when I saw her at Christmas. She had read it in the paper.

The smell of pitch has come into the house, making my nose twitch. I go to the front door. It's getting on for five o'clock, and the daylight is going. At the corner The Falstaff is already lit up in preparation for the coming evening. Plastic cones have been kicked about by children, and a shopping trolley is upturned on the pavement. Men have been tarring the road all afternoon from a smoking heap of tarred stones, and have nearly reached the top of the hill. Jenny's little girls play out, up and down the street, their hair flying behind them, and their hands, anticipating Christmas, clutch chocolate coins whose gold foil faces carry the big word LIBERTY.

'I'm being a crocodile, and I'm going to chew Cassie's toes!' The smaller girl rushes away with squeals.

At the top of the hill the pub sign creaks and swings, and the steam-roller pulls slowly away from the bucket of fire on the pavement, left to dash out its smoke in the cold wind.